MAN AN

ALFRE

MAN
AND THE VERTEBRATES

ALFRED SHERWOOD ROMER

*

VOLUME I

PENGUIN BOOKS
BALTIMORE · MARYLAND

Penguin Books Ltd, Harmondsworth, Middlesex
U.S.A.: Penguin Books Inc., 3300 Clipper Mill Road, Baltimore 11, Md
AUSTRALIA: Penguin Books Pty Ltd, 762 Whitehorse Road
Mitcham, Victoria

—

First published 1933
Published in Pelican Books 1954
Reprinted 1957, 1960, 1962, 1963

—

Copyright © A. S. Romer, 1933

—

Made and printed in Great Britain
by C. Nicholls & Company Ltd
Set in Monotype Times
Collogravure plates by Harrison & Sons Ltd

CONTENTS OF VOLUME ONE

CONTENTS OF VOLUME TWO

The illustrations in the photogravure
supplement are reproduced not from
original photographs but from the
previous edition

Preface to the First Edition

THIS volume owes its existence to the needs of the comprehensive course in biology initiated at the University of Chicago under the new plan of college work. In attempting to select appropriate readings to accompany the writer's lectures on the vertebrates and on the human body, it was found that existing works which adequately covered these fields were in general too lengthy and too technical for the limited time at our students' disposal. On the other hand, while well-written accounts are available for many of the topics considered, these failed to give any connected picture of the field of vertebrate and human evolution as a whole. In the present work the writer has attempted to bridge this gap, to give a brief but fairly comprehensive account of the evolution of the vertebrates and man with a minimum of technical minutiae. Several chapters on topics omitted in the course for lack of time or presented by other staff members have been included in order to round out the treatment of the subject.

The bulk of the work, including all sections to be used as required readings, have been submitted to the committee in charge of college work in biology for their approval, and many other friends have read and criticized various chapters. To all these colleagues, Drs G. W. Bartelmez, Merle C. Coulter, Ralph W. Gerard, Carl R. Moore, H. H. Newman, H. H. Strandskov, and Griffith Taylor, I am deeply grateful.

The writer has been strongly influenced in his treatment of human races by the stimulating ideas of Dr Griffith Taylor; his views as to racial evolution are expressed, with slight modification, in the diagram showing the phylogeny of human races.

The New York Zoological Society and the American Museum of Natural History, New York, have most courteously allowed me the use of numerous illustrations of animal types. A majority of the restorations of fossil animals are from a series of murals in the Field Museum of Natural History, Chicago, painted by Charles R. Knight. I am much indebted to the D. Appleton – Century Company for the use of a considerable number of illustrations from Snider's *Earth History*, published by them, and to the American Medical Association for similar borrowings from Harvey's *Simple Lessons in Human Anatomy*.

I am indebted to Professors G. W. Bartelmez and Griffith Taylor, of the University of Chicago, Associate Curators Harry Raven and Harry L. Shapiro, of the American Museum of Natural History, Professor Sherman Bishop, of the University of Rochester, and Dr George L. Streeter, of the Department of Embryology, Carnegie Institution of Washington, for the loan of photographs. Mr Llewellyn I. Price has contributed a considerable number of new illustrations, and Mr Brandon Grove has aided in photographic work.

I am greatly indebted to my wife, Ruth Hibbard Romer, for her aid throughout the preparation of this volume.

ALFRED SHERWOOD ROMER

Pelham, Massachusetts
1 July 1933

Preface to the Third Edition

WHEN this book appeared in 1933, as the first of a projected series of texts to accompany the new Chicago courses in science, both the author and (I think) the publishers felt somewhat like conspirators – pleased, but also a bit worried, at having produced a volume rather off the orthodox pattern of textbooks. Our fears were soon stilled by the cordial reception the book received, and I trust that it has served and will continue to serve a useful function. However, with the appearance of later texts in the same series in newer and more attractive formats, the earlier edition of the book appeared rather dowdy and old-fashioned in its make-up. I therefore welcomed with pleasure the suggestion that a thorough revision be undertaken.

In the text I have taken advantage of the fact that the type was to be reset to make a large number of changes. In many cases these are minor in nature, and about two-thirds of the contents remain very much the same. A new addition is the interpolation of a chapter dealing with the frog, designed to accompany use of this animal in the laboratory. The chapters on fossil man and human races have been almost completely re-written, as have the sections dealing with the higher fishes, and changes have been made to a greater or lesser degree in the discussion of birds, in certain sections of the accounts of the human organ systems in chapters 17 and 18, etc. As will be noted, numerous changes have been made in the illustrations.

The material is so arranged that various selections of chapters may be read to serve various aims. Chapters 1, 3, 5, 9, and 14 present the direct story of evolution from fish to man; chapters 2, 6-8, and 10-13 deal with various groups of fishes, birds, reptiles, and mammals which are of interest but not closely related to human evolution. Chapter 4 gives an account of the frog. Chapters 15 and 16 deal with human origins and races; chapters 17-19 deal with the human body; and chapter 20 is a discussion of embryology based on the development of man.

In the original edition I acknowledged my indebtedness to many friends and colleagues for help in the preparation of the book. Since that time, and particularly during the revision, many have offered aid, information, and useful suggestions, including: Drs Ralph Buchsbaum, Merle C. Coulter, and Herluf H. Strandskov, of the University of Chicago; Dr E. A. Hooton, of Harvard University; Dr J. H. McGregor, of Columbia University; Dr Homer Smith, of Bellevue Medical College, New York University; Dr Sherman C. Bishop, of the University of Rochester; Dr Edgar L. Lazier, of the University of California at Los Angeles; and Dr Robert Broom, of the Transvaal Museum, Pretoria. I am much indebted to Dr Carleton S. Coon for a critical reading of the chapter on human races and to Dr Harold L. Movius for reading the section on cultural evolution. Miss Nelda Wright has aided greatly in the preparation of the new edition.

Numerous, too, are my obligations to institutions and individuals for furnishing photographic material. A large number of prints have come from the files of the American Museum of Natural History, and Miss Jannette M. Lucas and, especially, Miss Dorothy Van Vliet were very helpful in aiding me in the selection of material there. The officials of the New York Zoological Society were also liberal in allowing me to draw heavily on their valuable photographic material. I wish to thank also the General Biological Supply House, Inc., Chicago, and its secretary, Dr A. S. Windsor, for a number of photographs, including an interesting series on *Protopterus*. Dr G. W. Bartelmez, of the Department of Anatomy of the University of Chicago, contributed a splendid series of photographs of embryos. Dr Coon has allowed me to reproduce a selection of his illustrations of European races. Others who have been of aid in this regard include: Dr G. H. Parker, of Harvard (colour changes in catfish); Dr Harold E. Edgerton, of Massachusetts Institute of Technology (stroboscopic pictures of humming bird and bat); Dr Florence de L. Lowther, of Barnard College (galagos); Dr Sherwood Washburn, of the College of Physicians and Surgeons, Columbia University (*Loris*); Dr John F. Fulton, of Yale University (*Tarsius*); Miss Belle J. Benchley, of the Zoological Society of San Diego (gorillas); Mr Harold J. Coolidge, Jr, of the Museum of Comparative Zoology (gibbons); Dr R. M. Yerkes, of Yale University (chimpanzees); Dr J. H. McGregor, of Columbia University (human fossils); Dr Franz Weidenreich (Peking man); Dr G. G. MacCurdy (Mt Carmel); Mr O. P. Pearson, of Harvard (shrew); Mr S. D. Ripley, of Harvard (spiny anteater, Papuan); Dr A. O. Gross, of Bowdoin College (heath hen); Dr H. C. Bigelow, of Harvard (teleost larvae); Drs Anton J. Carlson and Victor E. Johnson, of the University of Chicago (several anatomical figures); Preparator George Nelson and Mr R. M. White, of Harvard (paleontological photographs). Photographs of racial types were procured from the files of the Department of Anthropology, Harvard University.

ALFRED SHERWOOD ROMER

Cambridge, Massachusetts
4 March 1941

CHAPTER 1

Vertebrate Beginnings: Life in the Water

IT has been said that 'the proper study of mankind is man'. This is, in a sense, true. But, taken literally, the statement leads to an extremely narrow intellectual outlook. To understand the meaning of any other natural phenomenon we try to place it in its proper setting, its relation to other phenomena in time and space. There is no reason to treat ourselves otherwise. Man does not live in a vacuum, has not come out of a void. A fact of prime importance for an understanding of man is his position in the world of life, his relationships to other living things.

Man is a member of that series of living creatures known as the vertebrates, or animals with a backbone, a group including not only all the other warm-blooded hairy creatures to which man is closely allied but such varied forms as birds, reptiles, frogs and salamanders, and fishes. Their history is our history; and we cannot properly understand man, his body, his mind, or his activities, unless we understand his vertebrate ancestry. In the pages that follow we shall give a brief account of the back-boned animals, including the main steps in the human evolutionary story, and conclude with a brief description of man's body in the light of its history.

EVIDENCES OF ANIMAL RELATIONSHIPS

In attempting to determine the mutual relationships and lines of descent of animals, various types of evidence are available to us; the major ones are those furnished by comparative anatomy, by embryology, and by paleontology.

We may compare and contrast the anatomical features of adult living animals and from this study gain much information as to their degrees of relationship. The greater the number of fundamental structures which two animals have in common, and the greater the similarity in pattern of these common structures, the more closely do we believe these animals allied.

We must be careful, however, to be sure that the structures we compare are really the same and not two different ones put to the same use. For example, the leg of a cat and the leg of an insect are both used for walking purposes. But structurally they are entirely different (the skeleton of the cat's leg lies inside, that of the insect outside), and it is obvious that the two cannot be traced to a common ancestral source but have evolved separately; they are merely analogous. On the other hand, the front leg of the cat, the arm of a man, and the wing of a bird all serve different functions in life but have an essentially similar structure, many bony elements, muscles, and even nerves being common to all. These real likenesses, termed 'homologies', indicate that cat, man, and bird had a common ancestor from whose limbs, by modification, have been derived the varied structures found in these living types.

Comparative physiology offers a second mode of investigation of animal relationships. Such studies of this sort as have been made have afforded results of great interest. However, up to the present, much of the work of the physiologist has been of a descriptive rather than a comparative nature, and in considerable measure, confined to the detailed study of the functioning of the body in man and his mammalian relatives.

A check on the relationships of various forms is afforded by a study of their embryos, of the structural development of the unborn young. When serious study of this branch of science was begun a century ago, it was discovered that related forms generally have similar types of development. The embryos of men and insects have almost nothing in common; those of man and other vertebrates are much more closely comparable. Among vertebrates, the developmental history of reptiles is closer to that of man than is the case with fishes, and the unborn young of such warm-blooded animals as pigs or monkeys are even closer to the human pattern. These facts, discussed in chapter 20, in general tend to confirm evidences of relationship gained from other lines of investigation.

THE FOSSIL RECORD. A further line of attack on the history of living things lies in the domain of paleontology, the study of fossil animals. Comparative anatomy, studies of function, and embryology may enable us to deduce probable relationships and hypothetical ancestors. But it is infinitely more satisfactory to find, if we can, the concrete remains of the ancestors themselves in the record preserved by rocks laid down in past ages of the earth.

For many forms of life this record is none too satisfactory. Plant tissues are in great measure soft structures which are comparatively seldom fossilized, and, although we have considerable knowledge of the evolution of various types of trees, much of the botanical story cannot be confirmed by direct fossil evidence. Among the animals lacking a backbone there are a number of groups which have shells or other hard parts. Of these we have abundant records. But most of the important connecting links were apparently soft-bodied creatures which are rarely preserved as fossils. Further, the history of many invertebrate groups has covered a vast stretch of time, and the older rocks which should contain the early chapters of the story have been lost from the earth's crust or so much modified by crushing or heating that the fossil story they once carried has been obliterated.

With the backboned animals paleontological inquiry is much more fruitful, for several reasons. Almost all vertebrates have hard skeletal parts – bones, armour plates, or teeth – capable of fossilization. Further, vertebrates are a comparatively modern group. Our known history stretches back less than 500 million years. This (while a rather good stretch of time) is but the last third of the known history of the earth, and for all this time we have available for study numerous series of fossil-bearing rocks.

The study of fossils is a comparatively new branch of knowledge. It is only within the last century and a half that fossils have been generally recognized to be the actual remains of once living creatures rather than freaks of nature of some kind. It was not until the general acceptance of the evolutionary concept in the middle of the last century that their importance as ancestors of living animals was realized and a serious study of extinct forms begun. To-day we have a fairly good outline of the lines of descent of many groups of backboned animals, but none is absolutely complete. There are many gaps, many perplexities. It is obvious that we shall never fill in every little chink in this historical structure, for it is quite improbable that we shall ever find the remains of all the countless animals that have inhabited the earth. But year by year new fossils come to light which help fill the blanks in our puzzle. We have already progressed far in our study of the evolution of vertebrate life in past ages, and it is not too much to hope that, in the not too distant future, we may have a well-rounded picture of all the main points in the past history of our vertebrate ancestors.

A brief mention of the type of work done by the student of fossils may not be amiss. The average museum visitor who sees a mounted skeleton of an extinct animal has little idea of the great amount of work which lies behind this exhibit. Fossil-bearing rocks of any particular age are exposed only in scattered districts of the earth, and long trips are often necessary to reach them. Then, too, rocks must be not only present in a region but must be exposed at the surface. This means that most collecting must be done in treeless, grassless, sparsely settled, arid regions such as the deserts of Western America, those of Mongolia, or the Karroo Desert of South Africa. 'Bone-hunting' is not the most comfortable of occupations; even in good deposits, fossils may be very hard to find, and there may be many weary days of fruitless tramping over barren rocks before the collector finds a specimen worth excavating.

Then the work begins. If the find is of value, every piece must be removed with care and its position noted. Broken bones are often bandaged and plastered as carefully as a broken human leg, so that the fossil may not become irreparably shattered. The specimen is carefully packed to prevent damage on its long trip back to the laboratory, where work continues. The rock surrounding the bones must be removed (often it is exceedingly hard), all broken pieces cemented together and their positions determined, and, finally, the whole skeleton mounted. The mounting of a dinosaur may take years, and even some specimens no larger than a man's fist may be so delicate that months may be spent in preparing them.

Parallel with the laboratory work on the skeleton goes, in the case of new or rare forms, the study of the bones as they are prepared and the determination of the anatomy of the creature and its proper position in the family tree – sometimes a task of difficulty in the case of strange new forms.

Parenthetically, we may mention the popular belief that the paleontologist often restores a fossil animal from one toe bone. A century ago it was thought that if (for example) one found the body of an animal built like a horse, but with the legs missing, one could assume that the creature had hoofs. But – to follow this particular case – it was found that some such creatures (chalicotheres, chapter 11) in reality had feet armed with huge claws with which to dig up roots. Paleontologists have become chastened and more conservative. Parts of skeletons are restored in plaster in almost every fossil specimen, for few finds are absolutely complete; but, except for minor features, all work of restoration is based on our knowledge of the bones concerned in other specimens of the same or closely related types.

The scientist as well as the lay reader is curious as to how these old animals would have appeared and acted when alive and in the flesh, and numerous life-restorations of fossil animals have been made; a considerable number of them are shown in the present work.

Some of the restorations which we see in illustrated magazines are caricatures which never existed except in the artist's imagination; but many of the more carefully prepared restorations probably give us a fair approach to the actual appearance of the forms they portray. From the skeletons we get many clues as to the posture of the body, the style of walking, the bulk and position of the muscles which give the major contours to the body. Of the skin we know comparatively little, and in coloured restorations the pigment given the skin is a guess, although based whenever possible on the colours assumed by living relatives of the animal or forms which lead similar lives.

THE GEOLOGIC TIME SCALE

In order to use our knowledge of fossil forms effectively we must have some idea of the comparative times of their appearance and disappearance as measured by the scale set up by the geologists. A very considerable portion of the scientific work done in the field of geology has been devoted to the study of the comparative age of the various layers, or strata, laid down in the seas or lowland regions of the world in ancient days. On the basis of these studies has been erected a series of subdivisions of world-history, an outline of which is given in the accompanying table. We cannot, of course, tell the exact length in years of any of the geologic units, but the figures indicated are fairly good 'guesses', based on such data as the thickness of the rocks formed during any particular period of the earth's history and the present degree of decomposition of radioactive minerals laid down in them. The major subdivisions of the earth's history are known as 'eras'.

These are divided into 'periods', which may be further subdivided into 'epochs'. With this last type of division we shall be concerned only in our later study of mammalian evolution (chapter 9).

We shall have nothing to do with the first two of the five great eras in the known history of the earth, the Archeozoic and Proterozoic, for although there must have been much life in the form of plants and lower animals, our records of them are very poor, and vertebrates are quite unknown.

Our interest in this story begins in the third era, the Paleozoic, or time of ancient life. In the Cambrian, first period of this era, almost all invertebrate groups abounded, but vertebrates were still unknown. In the following Ordovician period are found rare fragments of vertebrates, and in the Silurian period we meet for the first time with good skeletal remains of early water-living, backboned animals.

The Devonian period, next in order, is often called the Age of Fishes, for these primitive vertebrates had by then become diversified and abundant. Here too we meet with the remains of the oldest-known land dwellers among vertebrates, the first amphibians. In the Carboniferous period (often divided into two periods, Mississippian and Pennsylvanian) amphibians had reached the peak of their development, and the first reptiles are encountered. The Permian, last of the Paleozoic periods, witnessed a decline in the amphibians and a beginning of the story of reptilian diversification.

The Mesozoic era is often called the Age of Reptiles, for it was during this time that there flourished many reptilian types now extinct. Most of the interesting dinosaurian and other groups had their origin in the Triassic. At that time, too, appeared the first of the mammals, destined to remain inconspicuous, however, during this era. In the Jurassic the reptiles appear to have been at the peak of their development, while from them had evolved the oldest-known birds. The end of the Cretaceous period marked the extinction of the great reptilian dynasties.

The Cenozoic, terminating with present times, is a comparatively short era, but one of great importance, for it was during this time that there took place the interesting evolutionary history of the mammals, and man himself appears in the final stage of Cenozoic history.

| \multicolumn{4}{c}{Synopsis of Major Divisions of Geologic History *} |

Era	Period	Important Geologic Events	Estimated Time since Beginning of Era or Period in millions of years
CENOZOIC (Age of Mammals)	Quaternary	Glacial conditions, followed by recent times	1
	Tertiary	Warm climates, gradually cooling. Continental areas mainly free of seas. Continued growth of mountains, including Alps and Himalayas	55
MESOZOIC (Age of Reptiles)	Cretaceous	At first great swamp deposits, followed by birth of Rocky Mountains and Andes, and cooling of climates	120
	Jurassic	Much of continent lowlands near sea-levels	155
	Triassic	Widespread desert conditions	190
PALEOZOIC (Age of Ancient Life)	Permian	Continued mountain-building; and variable climates including aridity and perhaps glaciation	215
	Carboniferous	Lands low and warm with seas over much of continents, at the beginning. Coal swamps, from which the greatest of our coal deposits come. Mountain-building toward end	300
	Devonian	Still considerable portions of land below water; evidences of aridity on continental areas	350
	Silurian	Much of land below the sea at first, followed by mountain-building at the end	390
	Ordovician	Great submergence of lands	480
	Cambrian	Lowlands and mild climates. First abundantly fossiliferous rocks	550
PROTEROZOIC		Great amounts of sediments in early part, followed by great volcanic activity and a long period of erosion. Little record of life, although presumably most of the larger groups of animals already established	925
ARCHEOZOIC		Great igneous activity, and some deposit of sediments, followed by widespread erosion. Little record of life	1,500?

* This table is arranged in the order in which the rocks of the different ages are found in the earth's crust, with the oldest at the bottom.

VERTEBRATE CHARACTERS

What are the characters which distinguish vertebrates from other animal types? What have men, birds, lizards, and fish in common? We shall discuss the structure of vertebrates, particularly from the human standpoint, more fully in later chapters. Here we may point out only a few of their more obvious characters, particularly those shown in the lower members of the group.

SYMMETRY. Vertebrates are, of course, bilaterally symmetrical animals; that is, one side of the body is in general a mirror image of the other. This character in itself distinguishes man and his backboned relatives from many other animal types, such as the jellyfish, sea anemones, and related forms constituting the coelenterate phylum, and the starfishes, sea urchins, and their relatives (echinoderms). In the sea, the ancient home of life, radial symmetry is characteristic of animals which are fixed to the bottom or float about sluggishly with the currents. Active animals, however, are almost always bilaterally symmetrical, and activity is a primary characteristic of vertebrates.

MOTILITY – SKELETON AND MUSCLES. The type of skeleton found in vertebrates is highly characteristic. Almost every animal of any size has of necessity some type of supporting structure to stiffen its body. Among other animal groups the skeleton is almost invariably an external one, on the outer surface of the body, as in (for example) a lobster or snail. Among vertebrates we often find, particularly among the lower types, more or less superficial armour; but the main supporting skeletal structures are always internal. Every vertebrate has a complex skeleton of bone or of cartilage ('gristle'), a somewhat softer, translucent substance. True vertebrates have a backbone (the vertebral column), a series of jointed structures running the length of the back and connecting at the sides with ribs which lie between the muscles of the trunk, as well as some sort of skull or other bony structure in the head region. Most vertebrates (but not all) have also a skeleton in two pairs of limbs (fish fins or land legs) projecting from the sides of the body. With the characteristic activity of vertebrates is connected the development of a powerful series of muscles for bodily movement.

NERVOUS SYSTEM AND SENSE ORGANS. All vertebrates possess as a main nerve trunk the spinal cord, a hollow tube running along the back (dorsal) side of the body. (In other animal groups where a nerve cord is developed it usually lies along the underside, or the ventral side, of the animal and is a solid structure.) At the front end of the spinal cord lies, in all vertebrates, the brain, a complicated central switchboard for the nervous system.

All familiar vertebrates have the same type of special sense organs that we possess – nostrils, eyes, and ears. But even at that, we may point out here, there are variations among primitive forms. Nostrils were, at first, simple pockets lying near the front end of the head for detecting odours in the water and had originally no connexion with the interior of the mouth, as they do in man and all air-breathers. Well-developed paired eyes are found in all vertebrate groups, but in addition there was present in primitive forms a third eye, the pineal, opening on the top of the head. This has been reduced to a small organ concealed within the skull in most living forms. Ears we think of as organs of hearing; but our ears are also organs of equilibrium, and this was quite probably their original function. Fish can hear, but only through vibrations set up within their bodies, for they lack external ears, eardrums, and all the mechanisms by which land animals receive and amplify sounds. The only portion of the ear which they have is the essential inner structures, a double series of liquid-filled sacs and canals lying within the braincase which mainly register the pose of the body and its movements.

BREATHING ORGANS. While land vertebrates such as ourselves breathe by means of lungs, primitive vertebrates were, of course, water-living types, breathing by means of gills. Some type of gill is present even in many invertebrate forms. Only among the vertebrates, however, do we find a development of internal gills. Water is taken into the throat, usually through the mouth. From there it passes out laterally through a number of paired slits or pouches in the sides of the throat to the surface again; it is in these slits that oxygen is taken up by the blood stream from the water and carbon dioxide given off. Gills are absent as such in higher vertebrates, but as an embryo even man goes through a phase in which the gill pouches are well developed.

BLOOD SYSTEM. The blood channels, the circulatory system, of vertebrates distinguish them from many invertebrate groups. In an ordinary (annelid) worm, for example, the blood passes forward along the dorsal (back) side of the body and returns on the belly (ventral) side. But in vertebrates, quite the other way, the blood is collected through the veins into a pumping organ, the heart, on the underside of the chest, then passes forward in primitive water dwellers to the gills, and, having been freshened in the gill membranes, flows backward to the body along the upper side of the trunk.

LOWER CHORDATES

AMPHIOXUS. The characters mentioned in the preceding section are those of a typical member of the vertebrate stock. If, however, we desire to look into the origin of vertebrates, we naturally wish first to descend the ladder of vertebrates as far as we can, to find as simple a form as possible to compare with lower animals. Some fishes are more primitive than others; the lampreys and hagfishes (discussed somewhat later) lack such typical vertebrate structures as jaws and paired limbs. But a far more simple form is the little animal, the lancelet, usually known by the scientific name of *Amphioxus*.

This is a small translucent creature found in shallow tropical marine waters, sometimes swimming freely about, but spending much of its life partly buried in the sand of the bottom with only the front end of the body projecting. Generally rare, it is so common in the Amoy region of the Chinese coast that it is sold in bulk as food in the markets.

Its general appearance is rather fishlike, but in structure it is much more primitive than any true fish. There are no paired fins or limbs of any sort, and no jaws, no bones or cartilages, not even a backbone. There is nothing that can be called a brain in any ordinary sense of the term, no ears, no eyes (although pigment spots in the brain tube appear to be sensitive to light), and only a tiny pit which may be the rudiment of a nostril. This form is obviously a much more primitive creature than any typical vertebrate.

There are, however, several important characters which show that *Amphioxus* is really a primitive relative of the vertebrates. This little animal has no backbone, no series of vertebrae running the length of the back and stiffening the trunk; it has, however, a fairly effective substitute in a structure occupying exactly the same position, known as the notochord. This is an elongate rod running the length of the body. Its interior is filled with a soft, rather jelly-like substance which in itself has no strength. But it is enclosed in a tough sheath, and the combination of the two gives an excellent supporting rod, fairly firm but flexible (a sausage has a somewhat comparable structure). The notochord is absent or much reduced in most adult vertebrates but is present in the embryo of man and every other member of the group. With development, the joints of the backbone grow around the site of the notochord and gradually replace it. Seemingly the notochord was the predecessor of the vertebral column; the lancelet shows the primitive condition.

Another vertebrate feature of *Amphioxus* is the well-developed nerve cord running the length of the body above the notochord. And a third good feature of resemblance is the presence of gills of the vertebrate type. Indeed, it would seem as if this simple little creature were trying to emphasize this point of agreement, for whereas a normal vertebrate usually has but five or six gill openings, *Amphioxus* may have several dozen.

The lancelet is thus a relative of the vertebrates, a point emphasized, incidentally, by the fact that the young form (larva) of the lamprey is very similar to it in structure. But it is a much more primitive type than any vertebrate and, lacking a backbone, cannot very well be included in that group. To express this relationship, naturalists have erected a major group, or phylum, of the animal kingdom, known as the Chordata, or animals possessing a notochord. Of this phylum the vertebrates are the major subdivision, while *Amphioxus* and a few other 'poor relations' of the backboned animals make up several lower chordate groups.

It is not impossible that the lancelet is fairly close to the primitive types from which the vertebrates have arisen, although this living creature has some specialized features.

TUNICATES. The tunicates, or sea squirts, comprise a considerable number of small inhabitants of modern seas. Perhaps the most generalized of the groups are the forms found as adults attached to rocks or other objects in shallow water. They are quite motionless and, in this respect, quite unlike the typically active vertebrates; nor is there any bodily appearance reminiscent of vertebrates. The sea squirt appears to be a nearly shapeless lump of matter enveloped in a tough leathery skin – the tunic which gives its name to the group. At the top of the animal is an opening through which water is drawn in. Inside is a large barrel-shaped strainer through which the water passes to flow out through a second opening at the side. Food particles in the water are collected at the bottom of the straining device and pass into the stomach and intestines. In the adult tunicate there is very little nervous system of any sort, not to speak of a brain or spinal cord. Nor is there any trace of a notochord or any skeletal system. Nothing more unlike a typical chordate could, it would seem, be imagined.

But examination of the straining barrel opens up a different conception of the tunicate's position in the animal world. The animal not only strains its food with this structure but breathes by means of it; it is, in reality, a very complicated chordate gill system, the true throat of the animal. We have here one good chordate character. And while that is the only resemblance to *Amphioxus* in the adult, the young tunicate rounds out the picture. The larval form is rather like a tadpole in shape, with a large head region and a slim tail. In the tail is a well-developed notochord and a typical dorsal nerve cord as well. The tunicate starts life as a small free-swimming larva, fairly similar to the lancelet in construction. Presently it becomes attached in the head region to the bottom; active life is abandoned, the gill barrel expands, and the tail – and with it nerve cord and notochord – disappears.

Seemingly the ancestral sea squirt was a typical primitive chordate, but the modern forms have become highly specialized and degenerate, a proper subject from which a scientific parson might draw a moral lesson on the effects of slothfulness.

ACORN WORMS. Quite different, again, are the acorn worms. These seashore burrowers are somewhat like the ordinary annelid worms in general appearance but have as characteristic structures a 'collar', in front of which is a tough burrowing snout or proboscis, the two sometimes resembling an acorn in its cup (hence the name). Despite the wormlike appearance of these forms, their internal structure is quite different from that found in the annelids. Strong proof that they are, on the other hand, related to the chordates is shown by the presence of numerous and typical gill slits. The nervous system is not highly developed, but there is a hollow dorsal nerve chord in the collar region, and a small structure in the proboscis is thought to be a rudimentary notochord. The acorn worms are assuredly far below the lancelet in the level of their organization but are highly specialized and hence not on the main line of vertebrate ascent.

VERTEBRATE ANCESTRY

The animals discussed above are typical of the lower chordates, the only close living relatives of the vertebrates. *Amphioxus* seems to give us a fairly reliable picture of an early stage in

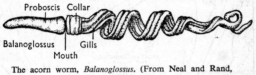

The acorn worm, *Balanoglossus*. (From Neal and Rand, *Comparative Anatomy*)

vertebrate development, but none of the forms mentioned has led us to connect the vertebrates with any other lower animal type. The main stock of the more advanced invertebrates lies seemingly among the coelenterates, multicellular animals with radial symmetry, such as the corals, jellyfish, and sea anemones. From them, or some form a bit more advanced, seem to have arisen two main lines of invertebrate evolution, one leading to the echinoderms, a second to the annelid worms, the molluscs, and the arthropods (or joint-limbed animals), a great group including insects, crustaceans, millipedes, and arachnids, among others.

Except for the molluscs, every phylum mentioned has been put forward for the role of vertebrate ancestors. Some suggest that the coelenterates have been the group from which the vertebrates sprang. This may well have been true in the long run, since these lowly animals presumably were ancestral to all the higher types of life. But may it not be that the vertebrates progressed farther along one of the main lines leading upward from the basal stock before branching out on their own? Can we not find some indications of vertebrate connexions in one of the more advanced invertebrate groups?

ANNELID WORMS. The annelid worms, which include not only the earthworm but a great variety of more highly developed marine types, have been advocated by some as our progenitors. There are a number of common features. The annelids are bilaterally symmetrical, as are vertebrates. They are segmented, each joint of their body repeating the structures of the one ahead; and vertebrates too are segmented, at least as regards backbone, muscles, and nerves.

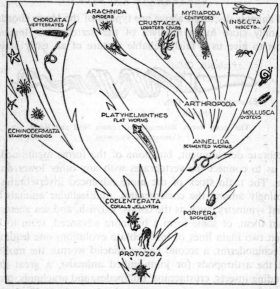

A simplified family tree of the invertebrate phyla. The chordates, including the vertebrates, are probably akin to the echinoderms (starfish, sea urchins, etc.) but only distantly related to other groups.

Annelid worms, too, have a nerve cord and a good blood system. But here we find marked differences from the vertebrate plan of structure. The nerve cord lies on the underside rather than the upper side of the animal, and the blood flows in opposite directions from that in vertebrates along the two aspects of the body. But, as in the figure overpage, these differences may be corrected if the position of the animal is reversed and the worm is assumed to have turned over to become a vertebrate.

It may be that top and bottom mean little to a worm; but the reversal of position raises as many problems as it solves. We must, for example, close the old worm mouth and drill a new one through the former roof of the head, for in both worms and backboned animals the mouth lies on the underside, beneath the brain. Then, again, where are, in the worm, the notochord and gill slits, those vertebrate structures to which even the lowest of chordates clung tenaciously? Their homologues have been sought in annelids, but sought in vain. There is little positive evidence for belief in the origin of vertebrates from segmented worms.

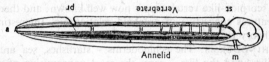

Diagram to illustrate the supposed transformation of an annelid worm into a vertebrate. In normal position this represents the annelid with a 'brain' (s) at the front end and a nerve cord (x) running along the underside of the body. The mouth (m) is on the underside of the animal, the anus (a) at the end of the tail; the blood stream (indicated by arrows) flows forward on the upper side of the body, back on the underside. Turn the book upside down and now we have the vertebrate, with nerve cord and blood streams reversed. But it is necessary to build a new mouth (st) and anus (pr) and close the old one; the worm really had no notochord (n); and the supposed change is not as simple as it seems. (From Wilder, History of the Human Body, by permission of Henry Holt & Co., publishers.)

ARACHNIDS. The arthropods include among their numbers some of the most highly organized of all invertebrates. It is not unreasonable to seek vertebrate ancestors in this phylum. The insects and crustaceans, most numerous of arthropods, have not been seriously considered in this connexion, nor have the centipedes and their relatives. A more worth-while case has been made out for the arachnids.

These forms include not only the spiders, mites, and scorpions but also the horseshoe crab (Limulus) of the Atlantic coast and a number of old Paleozoic relatives of this last type, the eurypterids, or water scorpions. The late Dr Patten, of Dartmouth College, devoted much of his life to the fascinating theory of vertebrate descent from the arachnid stock. The eurypterids, like other arthropods, were armoured types, with an external rather than an internal skeleton. But some of the early vertebrates were armoured too, as well as possessing deeper-lying skeletal structures. The armour of the water scorpions resembled to a considerable extent that of some early vertebrates. May not armoured arachnids have given rise to armoured vertebrates?

But there are numerous objections. Where, for example, have gone the numerous jointed legs in the water scorpion? There is no trace of them in vertebrates. Further, it is the top of the arachnid which is comparable with the top of the vertebrate; but in arachnids (as in worms) the nerve cord is on the underside. We must turn the animal over, and this destroys most of the resemblance. The anatomy of some of the oldest and seemingly most scorpion-like vertebrates is now well known; and there are no features suggestive of arachnid relationship. Interesting as this theory is, it finds little positive support.

ECHINODERMS. The echinoderms – starfishes, sea urchins, sea lilies, and the like – seem the most unpromising of all as potential ancestors of the vertebrates. They are radially symmetrical, in contrast to vertebrates; they have no internal skeleton, no trace of any of the three major chordate characters of notochord, nerve cord, or gill slits, and have, too, many peculiar and complicated organs of their own. At first sight one would be inclined not even to consider them. But here embryology sheds an unexpected gleam of light.

The early embryo of the echinoderm is a tiny creature, almost at the edge of the range of vision of the naked eye, which floats freely in the sea water. Unlike the adult, the larva is bilaterally symmetrical, suggesting that the radial symmetry of the starfish is a secondary affair, assumed when the ancestors of these forms took up a sedentary existence. This renders a connexion with vertebrates a bit more probable. Then, too, the type of development of certain of the body cavities is identical with that found in the embryos of some primitive vertebrates. And both in appearance and in basic structure the larvae of some echinoderms are so close to the larva of the acorn worm that the worm larva was long thought to pertain to some echinoderm type.

Here, at last, are some positive facts, and from a quarter where one would least expect them. No one would believe that man or any other vertebrate descended from a starfish. But the evidence from the larvae strongly suggests that long ago, in the dawn of the world, there existed some type of small, bilaterally symmetrical animal of very simple structure posessing many of the features of the larval echinoderm or acorn worm but lacking the specializations of either starfish or vertebrate groups. From these forms, by the assumption of radial symmetry and a sessile mode of life, came the echinoderms. But from these forms, too, seem to have arisen types which retained their original bilateral symmetry, and which gained specialized breathing organs in the form of gill slits, better possibilities of motility with the development of a comparatively powerful musculature and a notochord for its support, and better nervous control of activity through the development of a dorsal nerve cord. From this line, we believe, came the chordates and, finally, the true vertebrates.

This discussion of the origin of vertebrates has been based solely on the comparative anatomy and embryology of the forms concerned. We have no fossil evidence to support the theory of vertebrate ancestry advocated here, since the early ancestors of the vertebrates presumably were soft-bodied forms, possessing no hard parts, and hence incapable of preservation under ordinary conditions. We have no certain fossil record of lower chordates or chordate ancestors and very possibly never shall have. The oldest ancestors of the vertebrates are unknown and may always remain unknown.

PRIMITIVE VERTEBRATES – BACKBONE

What marks the first stage in vertebrate evolution? What sort of creatures were our earliest backboned ancestors?

LAMPREYS. A partial answer to these questions may be obtained from a consideration of the lampreys, which (with the related hagfishes) are the lowliest of living vertebrates. These forms, found in both fresh and salt waters, are in appearance rather elongate and eel-shaped but are far more primitive in structure than an eel or any ordinary fish type. There are no paired limbs or fins such as every ordinary fish possesses. Jaws are entirely lacking; there is only a round mouth (whence the term 'cyclostomes', often applied to these forms), which in lampreys is a cuplike sucking disc. These animals attach themselves to higher fishes and exist by eating their flesh. A peculiar rasping tongue-like structure forms a substitute for jaws. Instead of the normal pair of nostrils, there is but a single nasal opening situated at the tip of the snout or on the top of the head.

Internally, too, these forms are rather primitive and peculiar. They are far above the lancelet stage, for, in addition to the notochord, there are other skeletal parts of cartilage: a braincase, a highly developed set of gill bars of peculiar construction, and

the beginnings of a backbone. The brain is well developed, and
for sense organs there is not only the single nostril noted above
but rather rudimentary eyes and internal ears (although, incidentally, where normal vertebrates have three semi-circular
canals for the sense of balance, the cyclostomes have but two or one).

These odd forms are obviously highly specialized in many
respects but are definitely more primitive than any typical fishes
in two important features – the absence of jaws and the absence
of paired limbs. Here they seem certainly to represent a very low
stage in vertebrate evolution. But the lamprey as such is obviously
not our ancestor. We must go farther in our quest of a really
primitive vertebrate.

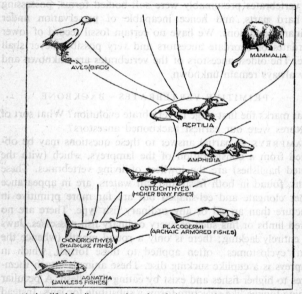

A simplified family tree to show the relationships of the vertebrate classes

OSTRACODERMS. Here we may for the first time avail ourselves of the knowledge gained from the fossil record. In the
second period of the Paleozoic era, the Ordovician, we find the
first faint traces of the oldest known of our vertebrate kinsmen
in the shape of small flakes of bone in rock deposits apparently

formed in a shallow bay in an old sea that once covered much of Colorado and other western states. It is probable that the oldest vertebrates were inhabitants of fresh waters, and most of the older rocks are marine deposits. Hence it is only when (as in a case like this) remains were carried by rivers to the sea that we can obtain any record of the early presence of backboned animals.

These oldest fragments, dating from a period in the earth's history perhaps 450,000,000 years ago, are not well enough preserved to give us any idea of the nature or appearance of the forms from which they came. It is not until a whole period later, in the late Silurian, that we first find complete skulls and skeletons of these most ancient predecessors of man.

And here we find ourselves in a quaint, bizarre world. These archaic vertebrates were water-living types, with fishlike bodies and tails. But, whereas modern fishes often have naked skins or are covered in many cases merely by thin scales or denticles, these ancient vertebrates were, one and all, armoured with thick plates of bone or bonelike material – scales over the trunk and tail, where motility for swimming was essential, and a solid layer of armour plates over the head region. This armoured condition has led to the frequent use of the term 'ostracoderms' (shell-skinned) for these oldest vertebrates. In their general appearance they were quite unlike the lampreys and hagfishes, in which there is no armour or, indeed, bone of any sort. But when these fishes are more closely examined, it is seen that there are real resemblances to the lampreys, indicating true relationship. Like the cyclostomes, these oldest vertebrates lacked any trace of jaws, the mouth being merely a small hole or crosswise slit; and there are no typical limbs or paired fins, with, at the most, a pair of flaps behind the head region or small spines at the sides of the body. Even in detail there are many resemblances between ostracoderms and cyclostomes. Many of these old fossils had, as in lampreys, a single nostril high up on top of the head, and the casts of such structures as brains and ears show that we are dealing with forms fundamentally similar to the lamprey type.

Putting together the evidence from both living and fossil forms, it seems certain that the jawless and limbless condition is one to be expected in the oldest vertebrate types. Ostracoderms and lampreys represent the most primitive stage in vertebrate evolution. But we have been loath to believe that the armoured ostracoderms were actual ancestors of later types; it has been assumed that the true ancestors of later vertebrates were soft-bodied forms which might have escaped preservation and that the

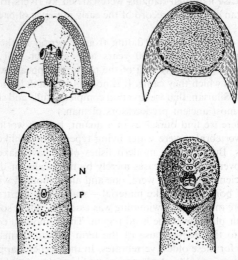

Upper and lower surfaces of the head in a Paleozoic armoured jawless vertebrate (*Cephalaspis, above*) and a modern, degenerate type, the lamprey (*below*). In both the nostril is a single opening on the top of the head. Behind the nostril is a median eye (the pineal) between the paired eyes. On the underside the ancient type had but a small mouth which appears to have sucked in nutritive material which was strained out in its passage to the round gill openings at the side of the throat. In the lamprey, with its carnivorous habits, a large sucking mouth has developed, with a toothed rasping 'tongue' in its centre (the gill openings, not shown, were farther back on the sides of the throat). (*Cephalaspis* after Stensiö: lamprey from Norman, *A History of Fishes*)

ostracoderms were merely an aberrant group having nothing to do with the line of descent of higher fishes or land forms.

Recent work, however, has tended strongly to show that some of the ostracoderms probably are exceedingly close to the line of descent of both cyclostomes and higher fishes. Bone, in the shape of both surface armour and internal skeletal parts, seems to be an extremely old vertebrate character. It is probable that many vertebrates now lacking such structures are degenerate rather than primitive. We know, for example, that such a fish as a sturgeon, with hardly a bone in its body, has descended from forms with a well-ossified skeleton, and it is highly probable that other modern forms which have no bones, such as lampreys and sharks, are in reality degenerate rather than primitive types. Armour was probably a character common to the ancestors of all vertebrates, and the ostracoderms are really an ancestral group.

VERTEBRATES VERSUS WATER SCORPIONS. But why should the early vertebrates have been armoured? An answer may perhaps be found by considering their habitat. These oldest of backboned animals were mainly flat-bodied, comparatively sluggish types whose lives appear to have been spent along the muddy bottoms of fresh-water ponds and streams. The absence of jaws prevented them from becoming predatory types, and the only mode of existence open to them was that of grubbers in the mud.

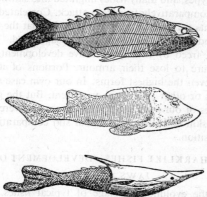

Some of the most ancient of known vertebrates. *Above, Birkenia; centre, Cephalaspis; below, Pteraspis.* These three grotesque little fish were jawless mud-grubbers in Silurian streams. (After Stetson, Goodrich, and Heintz)

The only reasonable suggestion as to the presence of armour is that it was for protection against enemies. But what enemies had they? Most of the larger invertebrates which one would think of, such as the ancient cephalopod relatives of the squids and octopuses and the larger crustaceans, were marine forms, living in quite a different environment from that of our stream-dwelling ancestors. We do, however, find that there was one conspicuous group of invertebrates of Paleozoic days which inhabited the fresh waters. These were the eurypterids, or water scorpions, mentioned before; indeed the two groups are often found in the same deposits and must have dwelt together. These old arachnids were, on the average, much larger than the ostracoderms. The oldest vertebrates were seldom more than six inches to a foot long, while eurypterids were, on the average, much larger – some nearly a dozen feet in length – and were obviously carnivorous forms with biting mouth parts. Apart from vertebrates, there are few animals in these ancient deposits which we can imagine to have afforded a food supply for the old eurypterids; and apart from the water scorpions we know of no enemies against which vertebrates needed defence.

Later vertebrates tended to increase in size, became faster-swimming types, and many fishes migrated into salt waters where they were comparatively free from attack. Correlated with these developments we find, in the fossil records, that the water scorpions dwindled in importance and disappeared. The higher vertebrates, freed by their progressive development, tended in great measure to lose their armour. Portions of it, however, survive in even the highest forms. In our own case we have no bony scales or other superficial armament. But the greater part of the bones of our head are dermal elements, covered, it is true, with thick skin and some muscle but still comparatively superficial in position.

SHARKLIKE FISHES – DEVELOPMENT OF
JAWS AND LIMBS

To reach the evolutionary stage of typical fishes, two great advances must be made over the structural plan of the ostracoderms or lampreys, in the development of biting jaws and of paired fins. Only with the evolution of jaws and teeth could vertebrates leave the bottom, where food debris accumulates, and become predacious types, preying on larger living things. With the development of this new mode of life, faster locomotion for the pursuit of prey became necessary, and most true fishes have ceased to be flattened types and have developed rounded bodies with a torpedo-like, streamline construction.

JAWS. The origin of the jaws is readily surmised by a study of the skeleton of the sharks. There are, in every primitive vertebrate, skeletal bars lying on either side of the throat between the

Cladoselache, a fast-swimming, sharklike fish with broad-based paired fins. (After Dean)

gill openings. These have two principal parts – upper and lower. The jaws lie in line with these elements and, like them, are composed of upper and lower parts, with a joint between. It appears highly probable that the jaws are merely a front pair of gill bars which have enlarged, have rotated their free ends forward, and have been pressed into service to perform a new function.

In our own head and that of all higher forms the upper jaw is fused to the skull. In sharks, however, the upper jaw is usually still a separate element which is only loosely attached to the skull. A detail of construction which we may note here because of its future importance is the fact that the main upper joint (hyomandibular) of the arch just behind the jaws is utilized to prop the jaw joint against the side of the braincase.

The origin of the jaws is fairly obvious in a modern shark, but even more so in *Cladoselache*, an ancient Devonian shark which had already become an active salt-water dweller. Frequent finds of this form have been made in concretions in the deposits from the ancient seas which once covered the Cleveland (Ohio) region and have revealed not only skeletal structure but even such details as muscle fibres and kidney tubules. In

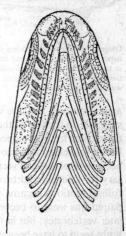

Lower view of the head and throat region of the Devonian shark *Cladoselache* to show the ventral parts of the gill bars and the jaws, seemingly homologous with them. The position of the nostrils (dotted lines) and orbits may be seen; teeth are in position along the jaws. (From Dean)

Cladoselache the jaws seem obviously in series with the gill bars behind them. Here, too, we gain a clue as to the origin of teeth. The
skin of sharks and other primitive fishes contains small pointed
structures, or denticles, which give it a sandpaper-like texture;
these are essentially similar to teeth in structure. In *Cladoselache*
the teeth which line the jaws are similar in appearance to these
denticles, and it is probable that teeth are merely denticles which
lay in the skin along the mouth margins and have become enlarged and used in a new way.

LIMBS. The main source of movement of a shark or any
typical fish is by sideways undulations of the body and tail,
which press the water back and the fish forward. Steering is
aided by the various fins. In all vertebrates, even the jawless
forms, median fins, lying along the midline of the body – dorsals,

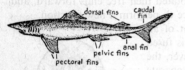

anal – help in steering, and
the caudal fin (also median)
is a major propulsive organ.
The paired fins, corresponding to our arms and legs,
first typically appear in the
jaw-bearing fishes as accessory steering organs. In most
fishes the paired fins have a
narrow base; in *Cladose-*

Diagram to show the situation of the fins in
fishes. The dorsal, caudal, and anal fins all lie
in the midline; the pectoral and pelvic fins,
however, are paired structures comparable
with our arms and legs.

lache, however, they are very broad at the body end and similar in
structure to the fins of the back. This suggests that they have, like
the median fins, developed as simple flaps from the body. In an old
bottom-dwelling ostracoderm, motion was presumably all in a
horizontal plane, and vertical median fins were all that were necessary for steering and turning. But with an active life off bottom,
rolling motions became possible and had to be controlled. The
paired fins were to become structures of supreme importance in
later vertebrates; but in *Cladoselache* and other early fishes these
limbs seem to have been merely stabilizing rudders.

EARLY SHARKLIKE FORMS. The oldest jawed vertebrates,
ancient ancestors of the sharks and higher groups, appeared by
the end of the Silurian and the beginning of the Devonian at a
time when the ostracoderms were still abundant. The jawed
fishes of this early day were, without exception, armoured and
had not begun the skeletal regression characteristic of sharks.

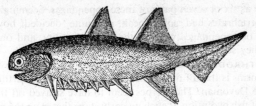

A primitive 'spiny shark' (*Climatius*), representing the oldest and most primitive stage in the evolution of jawed vertebrates. These little fishes, only a few inches long, appeared in the Silurian and were abundant in the early Devonian. Jaws were present but in a primitive condition. Limbs have appeared as paired fins supported by stout spines but were variable in development; the form shown sports five extra pairs. (Modified from Traquair)

Jaws were still in the 'experimental stage' and were sometimes but feebly developed, sometimes quite aberrant in nature. Paired fins, too, were quite variable. Most characteristic of these ancient jawed fishes were the spiny sharks (Acanthodians). These were still river dwellers and were still well armoured, covered with scales and plates of bonelike material. Each fin had a stout spine as a cutwater (fin spines, however, are not infrequent in living sharks). An interesting feature of the spiny sharks is that there was considerable variation in the number of paired fins. Some had merely pectoral ('chest') and pelvic ('hip') fins, corresponding to our own arms and legs. In others, however, there were as

Restoration of *Dinichthys*, giant Devonian arthrodire with a length of perhaps 30 feet. It is here shown pursuing the contemporary shark, *Cladoselache*. (From Heintz)

many as six or seven pairs of these appendages. Seemingly, these old vertebrates had, so to speak, not quite 'decided' how many pairs of appendages were of the greatest utility, and only later did they settle down to the orthodox two pairs.

ARTHRODIRES. A peculiar side branch of the primitive shark-like forms is that of the extinct 'joint-necked' fishes (arthrodires) of the Devonian. These types seem to have strayed off the main line of fish evolution at such an early stage that even the presence of true jaws or true paired fins in them was long disputed. *Dinichthys*, best known of the arthrodires, had by the end of the Devonian become a giant marine form, with an estimated body

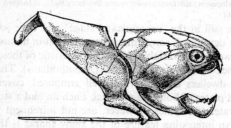

Side view of the armour of the giant arthrodire *Dinichthys*. The head and chest shields moved freely on each other by means of a pair of joints (a) at either side of the neck. The chest region was covered below by a broad plate which appears slender as seen in side view. The armoured region was about 10½ feet long. (After Heintz)

length of twenty-six feet, and some related types were even larger. The posterior part of the body was generally naked in arthrodires, but on the front half of the trunk the original armour was retained and elaborated. The head and chest portions of the armour were separately constructed but connected at either side of the 'neck' region by complicated joints, to which the name of the group refers. There were massive jawlike structures with fanglike projections; *Dinichthys* and his relatives were seemingly the greatest of carnivores in the ancient seas. These jaws, however, are thought to have operated in a peculiar fashion. While any ordinary animal opens and closes its mouth by dropping and raising the lower jaw, it is believed that the arthrodires held their lower jaws stationary and raised and lowered their heads instead!

DEVELOPMENT OF LATER SHARKS. While a few of the earliest sharks remained in fresh waters until the end of the

Paleozoic, the vast majority of these forms tended rapidly towards a marine existence and also tended rapidly to shed the ancestral armour. *Cladoselache* was far along in this evolutionary process, and in the Carboniferous there appeared the first representatives of the modern shark order. For several periods these forms were none too common, perhaps because of the rarity of suitable food for flesh-eaters in the ancient seas. Later there occurred a vast migration of bony fishes into the seas. These higher fishes have been the main source of food supply of the sharks from that time to this, and in the late Mesozoic and Tertiary shark types have been a conspicuous element, although not numerically a large one, in marine faunas. Living sharks range in size from the gigantic (but harmless) 'whale shark' of tropical seas to the small dogfishes abundant in coastal waters.

Once sharks had gone to sea, a possible source of abundant food for them lay in the great wealth of marine invertebrates, particularly the molluscs. Some members of the group became adapted for a mollusc-eating mode of life at an early date in shark history, but the skates and rays, living members of the shark group which live on shell food, are a comparatively modern development. The ray's mouth is filled with a pavement of powerful teeth for crushing purposes. Molluscan food is, of course, found on the floor of the ocean, and in correlation with this fact we find that in skates and rays there has been a secondary flattening of the body for bottom-dwelling. The pectoral fins have enlarged to form huge flaps at the side of the body and in some cases meet each other in front of the head. The tail has been reduced to a mere whiplash which in sting rays bears a poisonous spike. Another type of defensive weapon is found in the torpedoes, a ray type in which peculiarly modified muscles give off energy not in the form of muscular movement but as electricity. (Similar shocking devices are found in certain catfishes, eels, and even, apparently, in one of the oldest of ostracoderm types.)

An odd side branch of the shark family is that of the chimaeras, the ratfish and relatives. These are comparatively rare deep-sea forms of peculiar appearance, with a small mouth containing stout tooth plates capable of dealing with hard food; squids apparently are a staple in their diet.

With these grotesque types we end our excursions among the lower sharklike fishes. They have not, on the whole, proved a success; many types are quite extinct, and the surviving groups constitute but a small percentage of living fishes.

HIGHER FISHES – THE SKELETON PROGRESSES
LUNGS BEGIN

Much more important have been the higher bony fishes which constitute the vast majority of the world's present fish population and have occupied this commanding position since the late Paleozoic.

BONE. The term 'bony fishes' (Osteichthyes), which is applied to these types, is not an altogether fortunate one, for, as we have seen, bone is an exceedingly ancient character in vertebrates. But it will serve to distinguish them from the degenerate lampreys and sharks of to-day, in which bone has been entirely lost. It is only in the bony fishes and the land forms descended from them that this hard skeletal material has been efficiently and permanently used.

The bony fishes appeared in the Devonian, the Age of Fishes, and almost immediately rose to a position of prominence in fresh waters. In ancient bony fish the body was completely enclosed in bony scales, the head and shoulders covered with stout, bony plates. The top and sides of the skull were covered by bones superficially placed in the skin (dermal bones), and further plates protected the gill region, the shoulders, the throat, and the lower jaws. Still others were formed in the skin lining the mouth, fusing the old upper jaws to the skull and supplanting them for the most part. Other bony elements tended in great measure to replace the shark cartilages not only in the braincase but in the body and limb skeleton as well. It is of interest that the pattern of bones laid down in these old fishes may be traced, with modifications, into almost every later and higher vertebrate type. Almost every element of the human skull can, for example, be directly compared with a corresponding element in the skull of these ancient bony fishes. Higher forms have often lost old bones, but only rarely have new ones been added.

LUNGS. A still more characteristic feature of bony fish appears to have been the early development in them of lungs or lunglike structures. We usually think of lungs as attributes of land animals. But in two diverse types of primitive living bony fishes, functioning lungs are still present to-day, and there is strong evidence suggesting their universal presence in the oldest bony fishes.

The reason for this development of lungs may be found through a consideration of probable Devonian climatic conditions. The Age of Fishes was, it is believed, a time of violent alternations of seasons; much as in certain regions of the tropics to-day, there were rainy seasons alternating with times of severe drought. If the streams and ponds in which the oldest fishes were living tended to dry up, the water would become stagnant and foul,

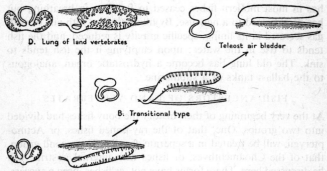

D. Lung of land vertebrates

C Teleost air bladder

B. Transitional type

A. Primitive fish lung

The evolution of lungs and swim bladder. Lungs appear to have been present in early bony fishes as simple paired sacs opening out from the underside of the throat. In land forms these have persisted but with improved efficiency, owing to foldings of the internal walls of the lungs. In most fishes, however, the structure has been much modified. The sac and its opening have shifted to the top of the throat, and the sac serves not as a lung but as a hydrostatic organ, the air bladder. These evolutionary stages are diagrammed above. In each case there is shown a section across the body and a longitudinal section of gut and lung to show the changes in their relative position. (Based on a figure by Dean

lacking the necessary oxygen for water-breathing. Such conditions would militate strongly against sharks and other lungless fishes. But if some sort of membranous lung sac were developed in the throat, a fish in such a pool could come to the surface, gulp down air, and breathe atmospheric oxygen in default of oxygen in its native waters.

The primitive lung appears to have been a double sac lying on the underside of the chest region of these fishes. This is essentially the type which has been retained and developed in land animals and is found to-day among a few tropical fishes which live in regions subject to seasonal drought. But in most later fishes the original lung structure has been much modified. It is obvious that a lung on the underside of the body renders an animal floating in the water top-heavy, and in most living forms the air sac has been shifted so that it lies above instead of under the throat.

Further, in times beyond the Devonian, climatic conditions appear to have been less fluctuating and the lung of comparatively little importance as a feature of survival value. This sac has in most modern fishes ceased to function in breathing but has been turned to a new use. By filling the sac with air, or with gas secreted in its lining, specific gravity is reduced, and the fish tends to rise in the water; upon emptying it the fish tends to sink. The old lung has become a hydrostatic organ, analogous to the ballast tanks of a submarine.

FISH ANCESTORS OF LAND VERTEBRATES

At the very beginning of their history the bony fishes had divided into two groups. One, that of the ray-finned fishes, or Actinopterygii, will be treated in a separate chapter. The second group, that of the Choanichthyes, or fishes with internal nostrils, will be discussed here. These forms have not, as fishes, been a success, but they are of immense evolutionary importance as the stock from which all land vertebrates have arisen.

The Choanichthyes in turn are divisible into two orders – the lungfish, or Dipnoi, and the lobe-finned fishes, the Crossopterygii, both almost extinct at the present time. Although the crossopterygians are actually closer to the line of ascent, we shall first describe the lungfish, since their living representatives show many of the traits expected in the fish ancestors of land forms.

LUNGFISH. The Dipnoi include to-day but three forms, one of which is present in each of the three southern continents. One is found in rivers in the interior of Australia, a second in the upper part of the Nile Basin of Africa, and a third in South America inhabits the swampy region of the Gran Chaco, over which the Bolivians and Paraguayans waged war a few years ago. It is of interest that these are regions subject to seasonal drought and hence are habitats in which lungs may be highly useful. The lungfish group derives its popular name from the presence of these organs; apart from two archaic ray-finned forms (mentioned later) which dwell under comparable conditions, they are the only living fishes which have retained functional lungs. Lungs are so vital a part of lungfish economy that they are apparently necessary for normal life as well as

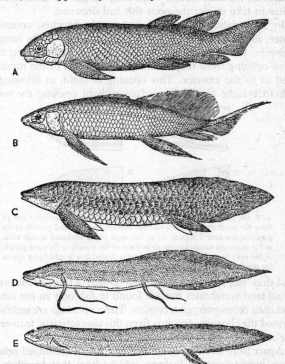

The evolution of the lungfish; a series of fossil and living forms showing changes in general proportions and fin structure. *A*, the earliest fossil lungfish (*Dipterus*). The median fins are all separate, and the tail tilts strongly upward; the whole appearance is similar to that seen in the related lobe-finned fishes. *B*, a somewhat later fossil type (*Scaumenacia*); the fins are tending to concentrate at the back end of the body. *C*, the living Australian lungfish (*Epiceratodus*); the tail is straight, and the median fins have fused into a single structure. *D*, the African lungfish (*Protopterus*), and *E*, the South American form (*Lepidosiren*), show a transformation into an eel-like shape and reduction of the paired fins. (*A*, after Traquair; *B*, after Hussakof; *C – E*, from Norman, *A History of Fishes*)

during drought. An American scientist, Homer Smith, in his book *Kamongo*, tells how for a long time his efforts to keep African lungfish alive failed because he thoughtlessly kept them in shallow tubs of water. Under such conditions they were unable to tilt their bodies sufficiently to get the nostrils above water to take in air; the poor fish had drowned.

In most fishes the nostrils are merely pouches, containing water, in which the olfactory sense functions. In the lungfish, however, the jaw construction has been so modified that there is an opening from the nasal sac to the inside of the mouth as well as to the exterior. This opening is useful in allowing the fish to breathe air at the surface without opening the mouth

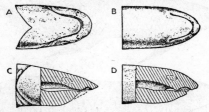

A, B, the underside of the head in a shark and in a lobe-finned fish to show the development of the internal nostrils by a forward growth of the jaws into the nostril region; *C, D*, the same heads sectioned in side view. In the shark the nasal pockets lie in front of the mouth; a forward growth of the jaws to the extent indicated by the dotted line would bring one of the nasal openings into the mouth cavity.

and thus 'shipping water'. Internal nostrils of this sort are present in all land vertebrates but are found in fish only in the lungfish and their crossopterygian cousins. These openings are technically termed the choanae, and it is from this characteristic feature that the name applied to such fishes is derived.

Apart from nostrils, lungfishes and their lobe-finned relatives have many common features which show that together they form a natural group. The modern lungfishes tend to be rather elongated and eel-like in proportions; but, as our figures indicate, the fossil record shows that this is a modern tendency and that in early days crossopterygians and lungfish were very similar in build. Of known common features we will here cite merely the significant fact that in both groups the paired fins have prominent fleshy lobes; they contrast strongly with those of the actinopterygians, which are supported only by horny rays.

The soft anatomy of the lungfishes reveals many structures in the nervous system, blood vessels, etc., which are highly comparable to those found in primitive land dwellers, and in the early stages of their development a lungfish and a frog show almost identical conditions. Lungfishes are thus close to the ancestry of land animals. But there are certain specializations which show that they are slightly off the direct line. The lungfish are eaters of small molluscs; their jaws are peculiarly modified for this diet, and the specialized teeth are fused into fan-shaped crushing plates. The lungfish are, so to speak, not the ancestors but the uncles of land dwellers.

CROSSOPTERYGIANS. The lobe-finned fishes, or crossopterygians, are the group which we believe to have included these actual ancestors. Lobefins were abundant in the Devonian, like the related lungfish; in later periods, however, they dwindled rapidly, and no typical member of the group survived the end of the Paleozoic. In consequence, our knowledge of them is more restricted than is the case with the lungfish. From the fossils we can gather much information about other organ systems as well as the skeleton, and we feel confident that in the older lobefins there were present many of the features, such as internal nostrils, lungs, etc., in which the lungfish resemble land types. The old crossopterygians had avoided the specialized diet and related dental peculiarities of the lungfish, and in almost every respect the skeleton can be closely compared with that of primitive amphibians. These fish lack typical legs, of course. But their fins are of exactly the sort one would expect to find in an ancestor of the amphibians. As in lungfish, the fins contain a fleshy lobe, within which are bony skeletal supports. Of these bones only one attaches to the shoulder skeleton. At its far end are found two elements forming a second fin joint, while beyond this there is an irregular branching series of bones. This is a pattern basically comparable to that of the leg of a land animal.

Typical lobefins were fresh-water fishes which, as we have said, early became extinct. Much longer-lived were members of a side branch of the lobefins termed the coelacanths. These early migrated into the seas and became rather specialized, short-bodied, marine forms, specimens of which have been found in various deposits up to the end of the Mesozoic, some fifty-five millions of years ago. No later fossil remains are known. Thus one has tended to state with emphasis that the crossopterygians are a group entirely extinct.

In 1939 a commercial fisherman hauling his nets off East London, South Africa, brought up a type of fish he had never

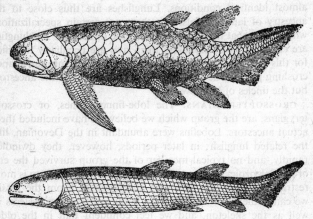

Typical Devonian crossopterygians, or lobe-finned fishes, closely related to the ancestry of land animals. *Above, Holoptychius,* a form which is closely comparable in general contours to early lungfish seen on p. 31. *Below, Osteolepis.* (From Traquair and Smith Woodward)

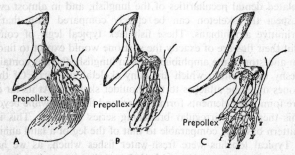

The evolution of the land limb from the lobe-finned fish's fin. Views of the shoulder and front-limb skeleton in a lobefin (*A*), a transitional type (*B*), and a typical amphibian (*C*). *H, R,* and *U* indicate the humerus, radius, and ulna of land animals and the homologous bones of the fish fin. The lines terminating in arrows follow the branching pattern of the fish fin to the parts comparable to the five 'fingers' of land forms (Roman numerals). There is evidence suggesting that early land animals had an extra 'finger' (prepollex) next to the thumb. (After Gregory)

seen before – a big, deep-bodied, five-foot fish with large, bluish scales. He brought it ashore as a curiosity, and, since its oily body was decaying, it was skinned, stuffed, and mounted. When a zoologist from a near-by college was consulted, he received a surprise which would have been little greater had he seen a dinosaur walking down the street. For this unknown was a coelacanth, a lobefin belonging to a group supposedly extinct since the days of the dinosaurs.

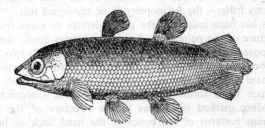

A fossil coelacanth. The coelacanths are crossopterygians, related to the ancestors of the land vertebrates. They have been long known as fossil forms, and the old figure shown here was based on material from Mesozoic rocks. That the restoration was essentially correct is proved by the discovery of a living coelacanth shown on plate 10. (From Traquair)

Presumably there are more of these fishes in the deeper seas off South Africa, but the international situation has thus far prevented the intensive search for them that would have been undertaken in more peaceful times.* We have noted that the coelacanths had taken to the ocean; this last survivor may be a deep-sea type, living normally at depths below those at which most fishing operations are carried out. It is, of course, a misfortune that most of the contents of head and body were destroyed in mounting the specimen. But we may comfort ourselves when we consider that in its habitat this fish had departed widely from that of its primitive ancestors and that its structures and functions, when known, will probably show highly specialized rather than primitive conditions.

* Since these words were written a second coelacanth was taken near the Comoro Islands in 1952, and was preserved in good condition for scientific examination, which is now in progress. [Ed.]

CHAPTER 2

Modern Fishes

WHILE the crossopterygians and lungfishes have been of major importance as ancestors of higher vertebrates, they have played but a minor role in the drama of fish history. Here the important roles have been played by members of the other major group of bony fishes – the Actinopterygii, or ray-finned fish.

As has been indicated, the group derives its name from the structure of the paired fins. Exceptional cases apart, these are composed only of a web of skin supported by horny rays. Flesh and bone do not invade the fin to any extent and are confined to its base alone. There are, however, many other differences between these forms and their cousins, the Choanichthyes, including marked differences in the structure of the scales, different patterns of the bones of the head, lack of internal nostrils, etc.

What the factors are that have been responsible for the success of the group it is difficult to say. One item of interest has to do with sense organs. Like most vertebrates, the Choanichthyes appear to have been largely dependent on the sense of smell for their knowledge of the external world, and the eyes were not markedly developed. In the ray-finned group the olfactory organs are present but relatively unimportant. The eyes, on the other hand, tend to be large and apparently are the dominant sense organs; this contrast is reflected in the brain organization. Eyes may thus have been important in actinopterygian history.

The air bladder, too, may have played a part in their success. Only the most primitive of rayfins retained a lung. In this group alone is found the transformation of this structure into an air bladder, a hydrostatic organ which, as suggested in the last chapter, may have proved of great utility, particularly in the seas which have been the home of most later actinopterygians.

Still more important in the rise of the rayfins may have been the mere force of numbers. In other groups of fishes there tend to be but relatively few eggs laid – from a few dozens to a few hundreds. Here, however, the eggs, although small in size, may number thousands or even millions for every female. Other fish, such as the Choanichthyes, may have gone in for conservation of the individual, laying fewer eggs, furnished with a more abundant food supply of yolk. On the other hand, quantity not quality has been the actinopterygian motto. Individuals may die in shoals, but the fecundity of the race will fill the ranks again in a short time.

PRIMITIVE RAY-FINNED FISHES. The oldest rayfins (the palaeoniscids) appeared in the Middle Devonian. They were, how-ever, not particularly abundant at that time and were greatly out-numbered by the contemporary lobe-finned fishes and lungfish.

Two living African fish represent the earliest ray-finned stage, although in somewhat modified form. The bichir, or *Polypterus* ('many-finned'), is the better known of the two. Like the oldest

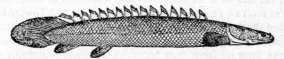

Polypterus, an African fish which represents a persistent (if somewhat specialized) descendant of the paleoniscids of the Paleozoic; the most primitive of living ray-finned fishes. (After Agassiz, modified)

fossils, the fish is covered with thick and shiny bony scales, and there are many primitive features. Most interesting is the fact that we find here alone, among living rayfins, well-developed and functional lungs opening in primitive fashion from the underside of the throat. This is to be correlated with the fish's habitat – the upper Nile and other tropical African areas where seasonal droughts occur. The fins have changed somewhat, however, from the primitive type, not only in the division of the back fin into the series of sail-like structures which give the fish its name, but also, most unusually, in the fact that the pectoral fins have developed a fleshy lobe. This last feature caused *Polypterus* to be included among the crossopterygians for many decades before its proper place was realized.

Two other types of fish, both present in American waters, also represent survivors from an early stage of evolution of the rayfins – the sturgeon and the paddlefish, or spoonbill, of the Mississippi. These types represent a somewhat more advanced condition, for they possess a typical air bladder rather than a lung. On the other hand, the fins have remained more primitive than in *Polypterus*;

the tail fin, for example, is still essentially sharklike, with the tip of the body tilting up into the upper part of the two-lobed tail. Again we find degenerate features, for the scales have been in great measure lost, and these fishes are long-snouted mud-grubbers with feeble jaws.

In the Mesozoic era the rayfins were the dominant fishes and were progressing towards modern conditions. The only survivors to-day of these intermediate members of the group are two common American fishes – the long-snouted, shiny-scaled gar-pike, common in rivers of the Mississippi system, and the bowfin, or fresh-water dogfish (*Amia*), a typical lake fish of the Middle West and South. These fishes are fresh-water forms, but most of the Mesozoic actinopterygians had migrated into salt water, and the seas were the centres of later evolution of the group.

TELEOSTS – THE DOMINANT MODERN TYPE. Towards the end of the Age of Reptiles there arose the teleosts, end products of actinopterygian evolution. No sharp line of demarcation marks them off from their ancestors, although technically they can be characterized by numerous details such as the assumption of a superficially symmetrical tail fin, thinning of the scales, etc. The teleosts form an overwhelming majority of all living fishes, including every fish familiar to us except those already mentioned – every food and game fish, every fishy inhabitant of the fresh waters of the northern continents (except their four primitive relatives cited above), and the vast majority of marine fish, numbering perhaps 20,000 species.

BODY FORM. The teleosts are exceedingly varied in every regard. In body shape and general organization rather primitive types include such familiar forms as the herring and sardine; trout and salmon are a little more advanced. While the fin rays of primitive types are rather numerous and flexible, many progressive teleosts have fins supported instead by but a few stout, movable spines. In body shape there are enormous variations. From such a smoothly contoured, fast-swimming type as the mackerel, there are transitions to such extremes as the stubby sunfishes or the elongate eel shape. The flounders have developed, for bottom-dwelling, a flattened body comparable to that of rays; but the comparison is only a superficial one. Seemingly, the ancestral teleosts had become so deep-bodied and narrow that the top-to-bottom flattening seen in the rays was impossible for them. Instead, the fish, exceedingly thin, has simply toppled over on its side. The head presents a peculiar lopsided appearance, mainly due to the fact that the eye of the underside, which would have been pressed into the mud of the bottom, rotates around the edge of the head in the young flounder to the upper side, where it is of use.

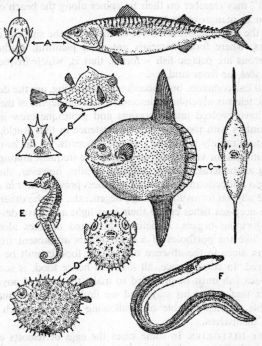

A number of living teleosts, to show the variety of forms assumed by this modern fish group. *A*, the mackerel (*Scomber*), a fast-swimming streamlined fish; *B*, the trunkfish (*Ostracion*), with a stiff body and only the fins movable; *C*, the marine sunfish (*Mola*), a very thin, deep-bodied fish adapted to quiet waters; *D*, the globe fish (*Chilomycterus*), with nearly spherical contours; *E*, the sea horse (*Hippocampus*); *F*, a common eel (*Anguilla*). (From Norman, *A History of Fishes*)

DISTRIBUTION. The primitive teleosts, as we have suggested, evolved in the sea, and the vast majority of the group still live in salt water. They have, however, returned in considerable numbers to the fresh waters which were the homes of their ancestors; the carp and catfishes are members of one teleost sub-group which consists almost entirely of fresh-water forms. Land and air are not, however, teleost domains, although there are so-called flying fishes which may glide for some distance above the waves, and a few forms, such as the 'tree-climbing perch', may clamber on their fin spines along the beach or even up on to mangrove roots.

In the seas teleosts are most abundant in the shallow coastal waters, where food materials are most plentiful. Rather less numerous are pelagic fish – forms, that is, which frequent the high seas far from land.

Still less common, but exceedingly interesting, are the deep-sea fishes, teleosts which have descended into the depths of the ocean and have evolved into a strange and grotesque crew in their encounters with the problems of existence in that world. Light decreases rapidly in intensity as one descends. As far as it goes, it is utilized for vision, and large eyes are frequent among fishes living at moderate depths. At great depths, however, the sun's rays do not penetrate; absolute darkness prevails, and in certain of the abyssal forms the eyes are degenerate. On the other hand, some deep-sea fishes create their own light and have developed light-forming organs, sometimes arranged in lines along the body like the portholes of a liner. Plants are absent from the depths, since in the absence of sunlight food cannot be manufactured. In consequence, all life, and hence food, is scarce. A deep-sea fish must be prepared to make the most of any edible object that comes his way, and we find forms with huge distensible mouths capable of swallowing creatures much larger than themselves.

LIFE-HISTORIES. In some cases the eggs of teleosts tend to sink to the bottom of shallow waters and undergo development there. A majority, however, produce eggs which float near the surface of the sea. Such eggs are tiny translucent objects which are laid in enormous numbers. It has been estimated that an average female cod may contain at the breeding season about 6,500,000 eggs. Most of these will fall prey to the vicissitudes of oceanic life. But if only two of the many millions which she may lay during her lifetime reach maturity, the survival of the race is assured.

There are many interesting variations in breeding habits. Some involve migration from salt to fresh water, or vice versa. The salmon group, for example: the Atlantic salmon spends most of its life in salt water but returns annually to inland streams for breeding purposes. This species may make a number of migrations inland for breeding purposes during its life. It is otherwise with typical Pacific forms. These salmon, once in the sea, remain there until maturity. Then they return to fresh water, and their life-cycle ends. After a journey (often long and difficult) inland to breeding-grounds, they spawn for the first and last time and, spent, die.

HISTORY OF THE EEL. Most interesting in many ways of all life-histories is that of the fresh-water eels. These animals abound in a number of regions, notably those bordering both shores of the North Atlantic. We shall confine ourselves to the European species, since its history is better known than that of the American form. Eels are common inhabitants of the streams of western Europe but have never been seen to breed, and eggs and larval forms are unknown there. It was, therefore, not unnatural that the ancients believed that they arose spontaneously out of the mud in which they dwelt.

But a century or so ago, however, it became obvious that eels migrated from and returned to some salt-water breeding-grounds. Every autumn mature eels migrate downstream to the river mouths, and every spring tiny young eels, called elvers, ascend into fresh water. The eel remains in inland waters for a period of from eight to a dozen years and constantly increases in size, the adult males averaging a foot and a half in length, the females a yard or so. Eventually sexual maturity arrives, and the eel, now silvery in colour, joins the autumn migration down to the sea.

Eels migrate in enormous numbers. One writer has estimated that, from a single lagoon on the Mediterranean coast of France, about 100,000 silver eels enter the sea each autumn and that the whole number leaving the European shore in a single season may be of the order of 25,000,000,000. Where do they go? It was at first thought that they bred in the waters not far from the river mouths they had left and that the elvers ascending the rivers the next spring were the product of these activities. But if this were true these well-fished coastal waters should yield plenty of breeding eels, eggs, and small larvae. This is the reverse of the truth. Of the milliards of eels which leave the land each autumn, hardly a one has ever been seen after leaving the shore. They simply disappear. Where do they go?

There have long been known in the oceans small fishes termed *Leptocephalus* ('thin heads'). Not merely the head but the whole body is thin, and these translucent little creatures, a few inches long, have very much the shape of a tree leaf. A first clue to the major problem was obtained a few decades ago when an Italian scientist kept some of these little fishes alive in his laboratory. To his astonishment they underwent a complete metamorphosis, or change of shape; the leaf-like body contracted into a thin cylinder, and the *Leptocephalus* became a baby eel!

Leptocephalus was known to be present in many areas of the North Atlantic Ocean. With this clue to go on, a Danish oceanographer, Johannes Schmidt, collected specimens from various parts of this great body of water. When the data as to their size, the time of year, and locality were plotted on charts, the eel story finally became clear.

Every spring, in April, eel eggs and tiny larvae may be found in a circumscribed area of the Atlantic, a few hundred miles in extent, south-east of Bermuda. It is to the depths beneath this spot that the adult eels travel to breed. The adults have never been found there; presumably they perish once their reproductive duty is accomplished. The young, however, do not remain on the spot or drift with the currents; they set a course for Europe. By the following spring many of them have reached mid-Atlantic and have grown to two inches or so in length. Another year finds the surviving larvae fully grown to three inches and arriving off the margins of the European continent. During the following summer and winter metamorphosis occurs, and by the following spring – three years after their birth – the elvers migrate upwards into the inland waters.

The American eel has a similar but simpler history. Its breeding-ground lies in the same general region but more to the south-west; and since the distances are shorter, the larvae take but a year to reach the coast.

We have, thus, the major facts of the eel story. But why this curious life-history? And how do adults and young find their way in these long journeys through trackless seas?

CHAPTER 3

The Conquest of the Land: The Amphibians

OUR story of vertebrates has so far been that of primitive water dwellers – fish and fish-like forms. This evolutionary history has not been unmarked by progressive features, for we have witnessed the appearance of jaws and paired fins, structures whose development enabled our earliest mud-grubbing ancestors to leave their sluggish life on the bottoms and become active, aggressive forms. But the greatest adventure of all still lay before the backboned animals – the conquest of the land, a feat which led to the development of higher groups of four-footed terrestrial vertebrates.

The change from water to land life was first initiated in the Devonian by the early amphibians and completed by the reptiles in the late Paleozoic; later, from reptilian types, were developed the warm-blooded birds and mammals. Once the water was left behind, there took place wide and repeated radiations of four-footed types. These land dwellers have adapted themselves to almost every mode of life on the surface of the earth and have, aided by the advances made during land life, taken to the air and reinvaded the seas. Snakes, birds, men, and whales are but a few examples of the widely varied types which have evolved from the primitive and ancient forms which in Devonian and Carboniferous times first left the streams and pools to walk upon the land.

PROGRESSIVE FISH DEVELOPMENT. It was not all at once, or in a single evolutionary stage, that there occurred all the many changes necessary for a fish's descendants to become good land dwellers. Some of the essentials for land life had already developed in the bony fish and, particularly, the lobe-finned forms from which the tetrapods sprang. Lungs, a prime essential for land animals, we have seen already present in the primitive bony fish. These forms too (in contrast with sharks, for example) had a well-developed bony skeleton without which life on land would not have been possible; the problems of bodily support are much intensified on land, and a backbone or limbs of cartilage would not stand the strain of terrestrial life without bending or breaking. Further, in the lobe-finned fish, we have seen developed a stout fleshy and bony lobe in the paired fins, which gave the possibilities of development into land limbs. Potential land adaptations were thus already being initiated in the fishes; and, on the other hand, land adaptations, as we shall see, are only partial in the amphibians, first of four-footed animals.

LIFE-HISTORY OF AMPHIBIANS. The amphibians are the most primitive and earliest known of four-footed animals; they are, as a group, the basal stock from which the remaining land vertebrates have been derived. Living amphibians include but three comparatively unimportant orders: the frogs and toads, the salamanders and newts, and some rare wormlike forms. All are highly specialized and have departed far from the first land forms.

The life-history of a typical frog, however, shows many of the essential characteristics of the class. The eggs are rather small and without the protective membranes or shell found in reptiles or higher types. Normally the frog lays its eggs in the water, just as has been the case throughout fish history, whereas the reptilian egg is laid on land. The embryo hatches out as a tadpole while still very small (for there is little yolk in the egg) and must find its own food as it grows in the water. Later, with approaching maturity, the structure of the body changes radically: the gills disappear, lungs and limbs develop rapidly, and the polly-wog becomes a frog; the animal becomes a land instead of a water type.

But even then the amphibian is not entirely freed from an aquatic environment, from the need of living the 'double life' to which the name of the group refers, for at the breeding season the frog must return to the streams or ponds; a complete adaptation to land life, a decisive break with water-living, is impossible.

Various devices have been developed by amphibians, which tend to avoid, to some extent, this necessity for a double mode of life and a double set of adaptations. In several instances the eggs are laid in moist burrows rather than in the water. Some tropical tree frogs never descend to the streams but lay their eggs in rain-filled hollows in the trees; some toads carry their eggs about on their backs. None of these or other devices, how-ever, has been a complete success, and it is not to be wondered at that among the salamanders, and apparently among many extinct groups as well, there are numerous types which have (so to speak) given up the struggle and have slumped back, reverting to a permanent life in the water and a life-long retention of water-breathing.

AMPHIBIAN LOCOMOTION. Among living amphibians the salamanders and newts approach closely in body form and general appearance the most ancient land dwellers. The body and tail are elongate; median fish fins have disappeared, but the tail is often much flattened and is still an effective swimming organ. The paired fins of the ancestral fish have been transformed into land limbs. These limbs in salamanders are quite small and feeble as compared with the legs of other higher types but are large compared with fish appendages. Salamanders can move their legs freely; but the body is still thrown into sinuous curves which push it forward on the legs supporting it, much as the fish pushes forward by pressure on the water which surrounds it.

PRIMITIVE AMPHIBIANS. But while the salamanders may resemble in superficial fashion the ancestral amphibians, such modern types are quite specialized and degenerate; the primitive four-footed animals from which all land forms have descended were quite different in many of their structural features.

Among the oldest and most primitive of known amphibians was a group (the labyrinthodonts) abundantly represented in deposits laid down in the Carboniferous swamps from which most of our coal deposits have come. One of these (*Diploverte-bron*) is illustrated. This form appears to have been, at its largest, about two feet in length, but some related types were as large as modern crocodiles, which they may have resembled somewhat in appearance. Much of the life of these ancient amphibians was still spent in the water, and small fishes which abounded in the pools of the coal-measures swamps seem to have been their main source of food. In their long, slim bodies, well-developed tails, and many internal features these early amphibians were still not far from the lobe-finned fishes from which they sprang, but the presence of limbs capable of locomotion on land is an obvious and striking difference. The skulls of these old forms were completely covered by an armour of bone, just as in their fish ancestors, and the older amphibians are very often called stegocephalians, or 'roof-headed' amphibians, because of this fact. (The very considerable reduction in skull bones in modern amphibians is one of many features which show that they are degenerate types). Behind the head in the fishes was a bony covering for the gill region; but the gills have disappeared in land forms, and this covering has gone with it. In fishes, a slit in the side of the skull just in front of the gill plates contained the small first gill opening or spiracle. This slit is still present in the skull of primitive land animals and still lodges this gill pouch which, as we shall see, now serves a very different function.

In fishes there was no special mechanism for transmitting sounds to the internal ear, which lay deeply buried within the braincase, but on land the problem of hearing is a very different one. Vibrations in the air are (except for something of the order of an explosion) too feeble to set up vibrations in the animal's body and reach the hearing organ in this fashion. For the reception of air waves, tetrapods, from the early amphibians up, have established an amplifying mechanism (cf. p. 310). Across the tube of the old spiracle, and primitively in the notch mentioned above, is a membrane, the eardrum, which picks up the sound waves. Between this membrane and an opening in the side of the braincase beneath it, which communicates with the internal part of the ear, there stretches in lower land types a small bone called the stapes, or stirrup; this is a modification, for a new use, of the hyomandibular bone which, in fishes, helps prop up the jaw joint.

The most striking contrast between the early amphibians and their fish ancestors is seen in the limbs. These were quite small in most of the early amphibians but already showed the pattern of the bony structures seen in land forms in general (p. 34). In the front limb of tetrapods there is always one large proximal element termed the humerus running from shoulder to elbow. A second long segment of the limb contains two elements – the radius lying on the inner (thumb) side and the ulna on the outer side, capped at the top by the 'funny bone'. Beyond these two bones is a series of small bony elements making up the wrist or carpus. Beyond this, again, is a series of long bones lying in the palm and each terminating in the free joints of a toe. In the hind leg there is a similar development, but the names are different. The first segment is the thigh bone or femur. The second segment contains two bones, the tibia, or shin bone, and the smaller fibula (needle bone) on the outside. Beyond these are the small elements making up the ankle or tarsus, followed by the bones of the sole of the foot and toes much as in the hand. In a majority of unspecialized land forms, just as in man, there are five fingers in both front and hind limbs. But most amphibians have but four front toes, while, on the other hand, there is some reason to believe that there may have been as many as seven fingers in some primitive land types. There is no a priori reason why five, particularly, should have been selected as the proper number; very likely there may have been considerable variation among early types before higher tetrapods 'settled down' to the orthodox five toes.

PROBLEMS OF AIR-BREATHING. We have little knowledge of changes which must have been going on in the softer parts of the body of these ancient amphibians, but we can draw many inferences from existing types as to the evolutionary processes under way and the new problems encountered in the development of land life. Chief among the difficulties in the transition between water and land life were those which have to do with oxygen supply. The fish lung is generally developed to a greater extent in an air-breather but never becomes a very efficient organ in modern amphibians. Much of the breathing is done through the moist skin, and some small salamanders rely entirely on this latter means of gaining oxygen and have lost their lungs. Reptiles and higher types use the ribs and chest muscles to fill their lungs. Amphibians have never acquired this method of breathing and use their throat muscles to swallow air just as their fish ancestors used those same muscles for pumping water to be utilized in the gills.

A further difficulty in lung-breathing is the problem of efficiently circulating the oxygen absorbed in the lungs. This is discussed further in chapters 4 and 18, so we shall merely point out its main features here. In fishes the heart receives only the impure blood from the veins and transports it all to the gills; from the gills only aerated blood is passed back through the arteries to the body organs. But from the lungs, now introduced into the circuit, the pure blood mixes in the heart with the impure venous blood, and this mixed fluid flows alike to lungs and body. The separation of the two blood streams has not been completely brought about in amphibians, and their inefficient circulatory system has probably been one of the causes of the failure of amphibians to become a successful group.

AMPHIBIAN ANCESTRY. Many features in the anatomy of the early amphibians point definitely to the lobe-finned fish as the ancestors of all land forms. In the skull pattern, and even in such details as the minute structure of the teeth, there is very close agreement between the two. The lungfish of to-day are quite similar to the amphibians in their mode of development and in many of their internal organs. But this merely means that the lungfish are related to the crossopterygians; were typical lobe-finned fish still in existence we should probably find them to be even more similar to the living amphibians in their soft parts. The one really conspicuous difference between the two types lies in the limbs; the fins of these fish were much smaller than the legs of the amphibians. But in some cases, at least, we have noted that the fins were essentially similar in structure to the land type of limb. A primitive amphibian was, in essence, only a lobe-finned fish in which limbs capable of progression on land had been developed.

WHY LAND LIFE? The most primitive of known amphibians were, as we have said, inhabitants of fresh-water pools and streams in Carboniferous and Devonian times. Alongside them lived representatives of the ancestral crossopterygians, forms similar to them in food habits and in many structural features and differing mainly in the lesser developments of the paired limbs. Why should the amphibians have developed these limbs and become potential land dwellers? Not to breathe air, for that could be done by merely coming to the surface of the pool. Not because they were driven out in search of food, for they were fish-eating types for which there was little food to be had on land. Not to escape enemies, for they were among the largest animals of the streams and pools of that day.

The development of limbs and the consequent ability to live on land seem, paradoxically, to have been adaptations for remaining in the water, and true land life seems to have been, so to speak, only the result of a happy accident.

Let us consider the situation of these two types – lobe-finned fishes and amphibians living in the streams and pools of the late Paleozoic. As long as the water supply was adequate, the crossopterygian was probably the better off of the two, for he was obviously the better swimmer; legs were in the way. The Devonian, the period in which the amphibians originated, was a time of seasonal droughts. At times the streams would cease to flow, and the water in the remaining pools into which the fish and ancestral amphibians were crowded must have been foul and stagnant. Even so the lobe-finned fish, since he possessed lungs, was at no disadvantage, for he could come to the surface and breathe air as well as the amphibians.

If, however, the water dried up altogether and did not soon return, the tables were turned. Under such circumstances the crossopterygian was helpless and must die. But the amphibian, with his newly developed land limbs, could crawl out of the shrunken pool, walk up or down the stream bed or overland and reach another pool where he might take up his aquatic existence again. Land limbs were developed to reach the water, not to leave it.

Once this development of limbs had taken place, however, it is not hard to imagine how true land life eventually resulted. Instead of immediately taking to the water again, the amphibian might learn to linger about the drying pools and devour stranded fish. Insects were already present and would afford the beginnings of a diet for a land form. Later plants were taken up as a source of food supply, while (as is always the case) the larger forms on land might take to eating their smaller or more harmless relatives. Finally, through these various developments, a land fauna would have been established.

OLDER AMPHIBIAN TYPES. Until recently the oldest-known remains of amphibians dated from the Carboniferous, time of formation of the great coal deposits. But already at that period amphibians were quite diversified, and we felt sure that their origin must have taken place further back in the Devonian, when the development of early fish groups was at its height, although no amphibians had ever been reported from rocks of that age. In the past few years, however, this gap in our knowledge of the ancestry of higher vertebrates has been filled in by the discovery of very primitive amphibians from the late Devonian of Greenland.

Many coal-swamp amphibians were still of the very primitive sort described earlier in this chapter. But besides these big amphibian forms there were numerous smaller ones, often highly specialized in various ways. Many had apparently ceased to leave the water at all and had much reduced limbs and a snake-like body. Others had huge flat heads with hornlike processes and may have spent their lives on the bottoms of the pools. Still other small but more normal-looking types may have been the ancestors of modern amphibians. Before the Carboniferous had closed, the reptiles, a group much better adapted to land life, had already sprung from the primitive amphibian stock, and towards the end of the Paleozoic amphibians rapidly decreased in numbers. A few large degenerate remnants of the old amphibian groups survived into the Triassic but then became extinct. Beyond that time the only known amphibians are members of the three living orders, which constitute but a small and unimportant part of the vertebrate life of modern times.

MODERN AMPHIBIANS. As we have noted, the living salamanders and their relatives are not dissimilar in general appearance and proportions to the ancient types, but in the skull and skeleton there are many degenerate features. As in modern amphibians generally, the old bony scales of the fish have disappeared; the skin is soft and moist and acts as an accessory breathing organ. Salamanders are consequently unable to expose themselves to dry conditions and when not in the water are usually found in moist wooded areas or buried under logs and stones. Most of them emerge on land as adults but return to the water at the breeding season; in a number of instances they remain permanent water dwellers. Gills may be retained throughout life. The mud puppy, not uncommon throughout the Middle West, is a form of this sort. In a few cases lungs remain undeveloped. Another interesting type is the axolotl, found in ponds and lakes in western North America, particularly in the Valley of Mexico. Under normal conditions this small salamander remains a permanent water-dwelling gill-breather. But, if experimentally treated in various ways (such as feeding it thyroid extract), the axolotl changes markedly, loses gills, develops its lungs, and comes on to land as a spotted black and orange salamander common throughout the United States. Evidently in the axolotl we have a form that (à la Peter Pan) never grows up; it is a permanent larva, sexually mature, but immature in other respects.

Other purely water-living salamanders may also have had a similar history. In the case of the mud puppy mentioned above, however, no treatment has been able to make the animal become a terrestrial adult; the animal has, so to speak, forgotten how to grow up. It is probable that this peculiar type of evolutionary development may have played a considerable part in the history of other animal groups.

A much more flourishing group of living amphibians is that of the tailless forms – the frogs and toads. Since they are amphibians, and since the amphibians are the lowest of terrestrial groups, it is often assumed that frogs and toads are, *ipso facto*, primitive land vertebrates. But this is really the reverse of the case; the frogs are in many respects among the most highly specialized of backboned animals. The specializations have to do mainly with their hopping method of locomotion. The back is extremely short; there may be as few as eight vertebrae, whereas a primitive land form would probably have had nearly thirty joints in the backbone not including the tail. The hind legs are excessively long and highly specialized, and the front legs, although more normally proportioned, are also much modified, with adaptations of the shoulder bones which break the shock of landing. It is quite probably their peculiar mode of locomotion which has enabled the frogs and toads, alone of amphibians, to remain a fairly flourishing group.

There remains for further consideration among amphibians only a group including a few inconspicuous tropical forms, the Apoda, or limbless amphibians. These are small, almost blind, burrowing animals which look very much like large worms and have no vestiges of limbs. These very degenerate creatures are not at all closely related to the groups considered above, and their fossil history is quite unknown.

THE FAILURE OF THE AMPHIBIANS. The amphibians are a defeated group. They were the first of vertebrates to emerge from the waters on to the land; but they were not destined to complete the conquest, and, at first abundant, they have shrunken into insignificance among four-footed vertebrates. Only by the reptiles, their descendants, was the land truly won. The reason for amphibian failure and reptilian success is not far to seek; it lies in the mode of development. The amphibian is still chained to the water. In the water it is born; to the water it must periodically return. We have noted various devices among living amphibians which have enabled them to circumvent this difficulty to some extent; but these makeshifts have not been particularly successful. The amphibian is conservative in its basic developmental processes. It is, in reality, little more than a peculiar type of fish which is capable of walking on land.

CHAPTER 4
The Frog

WE here turn aside from the general story of vertebrate evolution to consider in greater detail a common amphibian – the frog. In many elementary courses in biology this animal is dissected as a representative vertebrate. This account is inserted to accompany such laboratory work; in consequence, it is more replete with technical terms than are other sections of the book, and those interested only in more general viewpoints will be well advised to pass this chapter by.

While it is possible to study the frog without reference to any other animal, anatomical work is always of greater interest if done in a comparative manner. In chapters 17–19 is given an account of the human body, with a discussion of the historical background of its anatomical features. It is suggested that the frog might well be compared with man and that the description of the human organ systems be read as dissection of the frog progresses. With this in view, the accounts given farther on in this chapter of the various organs of the frog body have been arranged in the same order as is used in the consideration of human structures, and references are made to the pages covering the same topics in man. Many of the common fundamental considerations applying to both animals are treated in the account of the human body and therefore are omitted in the present chapter.

The choice of the frog as a favourite laboratory animal is due to several factors. One item (not a minor one in these days of restricted college budgets) is the fact that it is common, readily available, and hence inexpensive. There are, however, good scientific grounds for its selection. As an amphibian it represents a group halfway up the family tree from fish to mammal – an 'average' vertebrate, better suited for use than either extreme type if but one form is to be studied.

It must be pointed out, of course, that even this animal has its disadvantages. We have noted earlier that modern amphibians are somewhat degenerate in their skeletal system, and the frog is no exception to this condition. Further, the jumping habits of the frogs have caused great modifications of the limbs, so that these appendages are to be considered as highly specialized structures. However, apart from features of the skeleton and muscles, the frog appears to have adhered rather closely to the general pattern found in primitive land-dwelling vertebrates.

THE LIFE OF THE FROG

The forms most frequently used in the laboratory are members of the typical frog genus *Rana*. The bullfrog, *Rana catesbiana*, is an exceptionally large form; *R. pipiens*, the leopard or grass frog, is the commonest of American species. The bullfrog tends to spend much of his life immersed. The leopard frog is more of a land dweller; in damp weather he may wander far from the water but is commonly found along stream banks, ready to leap and submerge at an instant's notice.

FOOD. Adult frogs are purely carnivorous in a broad sense of the term – eaters, that is, of animal food. Since they are of modest size, the food supply mainly consists of invertebrates. Earthworms, insects, insect larvae, and spiders are favourite foods. However, they have no compunction against eating other vertebrates, and minnows, tadpoles, and even smaller frogs may form additions to the diet. The frog tends to snap instinctively at any small moving object near by (such as a bit of red flannel!). The teeth, however, are relatively feeble; an important method of obtaining food lies in the protrusibility of the tongue. This organ is highly developed, attached anteriorly, and normally lies with its free tip turned backward in the mouth. From this position it may be flipped out suddenly to gain contact with a fly or other desired titbit. The tip is sticky, so that the object touched adheres to it. A reverse flip, the food is in the mouth and is swallowed without further ado. The protrusion of the tongue is brought about by a peculiar mechanism. A large sac in the floor of the mouth suddenly fills with lymph and pushes the tongue upwards and forward.

ENEMIES. The frog has, in turn, numerous enemies. Man, either in pursuit of frogs' legs or in search of your laboratory animal, is a major factor in frog destruction. Frogs offer a substantial and favoured food supply for snakes; various birds and some mammals and even fishes prey upon them. The tadpoles are, of course, much more susceptible to attack, and their enemies include not only vertebrates but a number of aquatic insects; under ordinary conditions only a small percentage of the larval frogs ever reach the adult stage. Still other enemies are parasites of various sorts. Leeches suck their blood, and there are numerous internal parasites such as flukes, roundworms, numerous protozoan species, and even parasitic plants which invade their tissues.

LOCOMOTION. The locomotor abilities of the frog are highly useful to him in escaping from his major enemies, for he is an accomplished jumper and swimmer. The front legs are of use mainly to support the head and chest and break the force of the fall on landing; the hop is accomplished by a sudden straightening (extension) of the hind legs, which in resting pose are flexed in readiness. A frog jump under good conditions is well short of a yard (Calaveras County jumping contests not considered). In swimming the front legs are little used; propulsion is accomplished by alternate kicks of the hind legs, which push the webbed toes against the water. A favoured resting position is one in which the frog floats in the water in a sprawled position with only nose and eyes protruding; the level at which it floats may be regulated by filling or emptying the lungs and thus altering the specific gravity of the animal as a whole. Diving from the bank begins as an ordinary leap, followed by a vigorous downward swim. To dive from the floating position, the frog first gives itself a vigorous push back and down to 'submerge', then tilts the body downward to begin its swim to cover.

Besides flight, other factors help escape from enemies. Some of the skin glands secrete a mildly poisonous material which makes some animals avoid the frog. By puffing himself full of air a frog may become a round and slippery object, difficult for its enemy to swallow.

ANNUAL LIFE-CYCLE. The activities of frogs vary greatly with the seasons, particularly in temperate climates. The animal is a cold-blooded form, that is, it is unable to maintain a constant body temperature; hence in the winter it must hibernate, and so it burrows in the mud to avoid freezing temperatures. During this season the internal activities of the body go on at a much reduced rate, drawing for fuel upon food materials stored in the body, particularly in the liver and muscles. With the coming of spring the frog becomes very active. The sex organs develop greatly, the body of the female fills with eggs, and the breeding season arrives. Once the eggs are laid, life goes on at a slower tempo. During summer and autumn new stores of food are laid up against the approach of cold weather.

BREEDING. In the grass frog the breeding season commonly occurs some time during April, depending upon the climate of the region concerned and the nature of the season – the warmer the sooner. Frogs are, at other seasons, essentially unsociable and solitary in their habits. At the breeding season, however, they become highly gregarious and congregate in large numbers in shallow bodies of water. Fertilization is external, the male clasping the female and discharging sperms which fertilize the eggs as they emerge. The clasping movement is a readily excitable reflex action of the male; typically, male and female remain clasped for several days before the eggs are laid.

GENERAL FEATURES OF THE FROG BODY

BODY REGIONS. In its contours the frog body shows a division into three regions – head, neck, and trunk – found in all higher vertebrates. In the fish there was no distinctive neck. In the frog, with the disappearance of the gills, which once lay in this area, a neck appears. It is, however, shorter than in reptiles or higher groups, and there is in consequence relatively little freedom of motion of the head on the body. The trunk is much shorter than in typical vertebrates. A marked specialization of the frog is the reduction of the tail; only a rudimentary stump remains, concealed in the general contours of the body. The hind legs are developed to an unusual degree, equalled elsewhere only by man and some other bipeds. These various specializations of the frog are to be associated with its peculiar leaping habits.

ORIENTATION. In dissecting or describing a vertebrate, attention must be paid to terms used to describe the relative position of various parts and organs. The frog is, of course, bilaterally symmetrical, the right and left sides fundamentally mirror images of one another. The direction in which the animal moves (here the head end) is termed 'anterior', the opposite end 'posterior'. Upper and lower surfaces are called 'dorsal' and 'ventral' (Latin for 'back' and 'belly'). An annoying feature in the attempt to compare any four-footed animal with man lies in the fact that man's upright posture causes changes in directional terms. Since anterior means the direction in which an animal moves, this term in man becomes the same as ventral, and posterior the same as dorsal. We thus need new scientific terms for the up-and-down directions in man; these are supplied by using 'superior' and 'inferior'. The confusion that can be (and is) caused by this shift in posture can be readily imagined.

It must be remembered that most diagrams of body organs are drawn from the ventral side, as they are seen in the dissection of the abdomen. The right side of the animal is thus to the reader's left and vice versa.

SUPERFICIAL FEATURES. Most of the frog body is covered with a soft, moist skin, interrupted by a number of openings or other topographic markers. At the front is the widely gaping mouth; just above its anterior end are the external openings of the nostrils (or nares). Farther back on the head are the prominent eyes and the large eardrums. At the posterior end of the body is found the opening of the cloaca, a pocket into which open not only the digestive tract but also the tubes carrying urinary and reproductive products.

BODY CAVITIES. When the dissection of the internal organs begins it will be found that most of them lie packed in compact fashion in a large cavity – the body cavity, or coelom. Here are found most of the digestive organs – stomach, intestines, liver, and pancreas – as well as the reproductive organs and spleen, while the kidneys are exposed on the back wall. In mammals the lungs lie in separate compartments, separated from the abdomen by a muscular partition, the diaphragm; but in the frog the lungs extend freely into the general cavity. As in every vertebrate, however, the heart occupies a separate pericardial cavity.

The coelom is lined by a thin but continuous membrane known as the peritoneum. This covers not merely the outer walls but also all the contained organs. These do not 'float' freely in the body cavity but are attached to the walls by folds of the membrane, called mesenteries. The most important mesentery descends from the midline of the back wall of the abdominal cavity to anchor the stomach and intestine in place.

SKIN

In the frog, as in every vertebrate, the skin consists of two layers. The more superficial is the epidermis, consisting of a sheet of cells which forms a moist and thin but continuous outer covering. Deeper lies the dermis, mainly a feltlike mass of connective-tissue fibres but containing blood vessels, nerves, and sensory structures. In its skin the typical modern amphibian differs markedly from both its fish ancestors and the reptiles. The fish was covered by thick, bony scales placed in the dermis; the frog has lost all trace of these structures. On the other hand, typical reptiles have acquired superficial scales, or scutes, formed by deposits of horny material in the epidermis. Such scales are lacking in amphibians, although slight deposits of horn may form in the skin in some cases. The frog is thus left without the protection of either type of scales, and its soft skin makes it necessary for the animal to stay in damp environments to prevent excessive drying. Nevertheless, this type of skin has one advantage. It is a moist membrane which is capable of absorbing oxygen and giving off carbon dioxide; richly supplied with blood vessels, it acts as an accessory lung.

The skin contains numerous glands of simple construction, essentially globular pockets in the epidermis. Most of these secrete a mucous material which keeps the skin moist. Relatively few in number are larger glands which produce an acrid fluid thought to be poisonous in nature. While this appears to be relatively ineffective, certain toads secrete definitely poisonous materials.

Just beneath the epidermis is a layer of cells containing pigments of at least two types – one dark, one yellow – and crystalline granules. Combinations of these elements in different proportions and positions give the green, brown, and other frog colours. Further, the colours in many cases are not fixed but may show changes, owing to expansion or contraction of pigment-bearing cells or to changes in their relative positions.

NERVOUS SYSTEM *

In the nature of their nervous tissues in general – the spinal cord, the peripheral nerves, and the autonomic nervous system – the

* Cf. pp. 286–98.

frog and man are essentially similar. In fact, apart from the brain, the only noteworthy difference between the two is that in the frog the body is so shortened that there are but ten pairs of spinal nerves in contrast to three times that number in man.

Even in the brain many features are closely comparable with those seen in man. At the back end of the frog brain is the medulla oblongata, which appears in general structure to be little more than an expanded portion of the spinal cord with which it is continuous. In the medulla are carried out many of the more automatic nervous activities of the frog body, and to this region of the brain attach most of the cranial nerves. A projection above the front end of the medulla is the cerebellum, associated with posture and muscular co-ordination. This structure is much smaller in the frog than in most vertebrates.

Farther forward, the only notable feature of the midbrain region is the pair of dorsal swellings, the optic lobes to which in the frog (although not in man) run most of the nerve fibres from the eyes. A bit farther forward, in a region anatomically considered to belong to the forebrain, in a general sense, is a pronounced ventral swelling in the neighbourhood of the optic

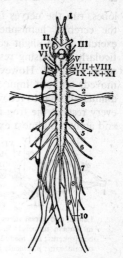

The nervous system of the frog seen from the ventral side. At the top, the ventral surface of the brain, continuing into the spinal cord. On the left side of the figure the ganglia and trunk of the autonomic ('sympathetic') nervous system are shown in black. The cranial nerves are labelled in Roman numerals, the ten spinal nerves in Arabic. Spinal nerves 2 and 3 form the brachial plexus for the arm, and components of nerves 7–10 form a similar plexus innervating the hind leg. (After Ecker and Wiedersheim)

nerves – the infundibulum. Just below and behind it is a rounded (readily detached) structure – the hypophysis. The two together form the pituitary, a vitally important gland of internal secretion.

It is only in its most anterior portion that the frog brain, persistently primitive, differs radically from that of man. Here, in the frog, are found small, paired swellings, each somewhat constricted at midlength. Into the front halves, termed olfactory lobes, run the nerves from the nostrils; the back portions are the cerebral hemispheres. The frog hemispheres appear to exercise some slight control over the animal's activities, particularly in causing response to stimulus received through the sense of smell. However, if the hemispheres are carefully removed, without injury to other parts of the brain, and the animal allowed to recover from shock, it is found that in almost every respect the frog is capable of carrying on his normal life and activities almost exactly as before.

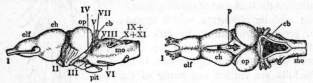

Lateral and dorsal views of the frog brain. The cranial nerves are labelled in Roman numerals in the lateral view; *cb*, cerebellum; *ch*, cerebral hemispheres; *mo*, medulla oblongata; *olf*, olfactory lobes; *op*, optic lobes of midbrain; *p*, pineal; *pit*, pituitary. (After Wiedersheim)

Far different, of course, is the situation in man. The human brain is notable for the enormous expansion of these same cerebral hemispheres, which have grown so as to exceed greatly in bulk all the rest of the brain together and have come to be the directing centres for much of the body's activities – the seat of consciousness and memory.

The frog possesses ten cranial nerves, comparable in major features to the first ten found in man. In man there is a well-developed twelfth nerve, absent in the existing amphibians, but found in reptiles, birds, and other mammals as well. Its absence in the frog has often been thought to be a primitive character. However, there is considerable evidence that it was present in primitive amphibians; here, as in other features, the frog is a bit degenerate.

SENSE ORGANS *

NOSE. Since the internal openings of the nostrils lie almost immediately below the external ones, there is no opportunity for the development of large nasal passages in the frog. Nevertheless there are small, well developed olfactory sacs folded in a complicated fashion, which appear to furnish the frog with important sensory information.

* Cf. pp. 298–313.

EYE. The fundamental pattern of the eye is similar in frog and man, but there are numerous differences in details of construction. Lids are present but are poorly developed; they cannot close of themselves, and the eye is shut by pulling the eyeball back into its socket. On closure, a thin membrane attached to the lower lid and called a nictitating membrane covers over much of the surface. The lens is nearly spherical and of a 'fixed focus' type and cannot change either position or shape to accommodate for near or far vision. The optical properties are such that the frog is near-sighted on land, far-sighted with the eye immersed in water. As in all typical vertebrates, the retina contains both rod and cone cells. In man the latter, which make for colour vision and clear perception of detail, are concentrated in a central area; in the frog the two types are scattered throughout, and hence we may assume that visual acuity is less pronounced. Further, the frog lacks the stereoscopic depth effects possible in man and many other mammals. As noted in the human discussion, this type of vision is rendered possible by a sorting-out of the nerve fibres from the eyes as they enter the brain. This does not occur in the frog.

The frog is, when at rest, popeyed, the eyeballs projecting prominently from their sockets but readily withdrawn. These movements are accomplished by the development of two extra muscles in addition to the six which in all typical vertebrates perform the usual rotary motions of the eyeball.

Primitive vertebrates possessed a third, median eye between the members of the normal pair; this is lost in most living forms, but the structure often remains, as in man, in the form of a pineal body attached to the brain. In the frog the pineal body has almost completely disappeared but may be sometimes identified as a tiny pigmented spot in the skin between the eyes, completely separated from the brain.

EAR. The frog lacks the external tube of the ear seen in mammals, and the prominent ear-drum is exposed on the surface. Within the drum is a middle-ear cavity communicating with the mouth (as in man) by a eustachian tube. A single bone crosses this cavity to carry vibrations from the drum to the inner ear, buried in the braincase. In man three ossicles are present here. That of the frog corresponds to the inner of the three, the stapes, and hence may be so termed (although usually designated as the columella). The other two ear ossicles of the mammal still retain their primitive function in the bones of the jaw joint.

The system of canals and sacs in the inner ear, recording body balance and motion, are the same as in man. The hearing part of the structure is, however, poorly developed; instead of the coiled cochlea of the mammal, there is but a small patch of tissue associated with sound reception. This suggests that, although the frog can hear, it lacks the ability to discriminate between tones of various pitch, as is the case in animals with a cochlea. Bass and soprano may be one to the frog.

LATERAL-LINE ORGANS. Fish possess a system of sensory organs arranged in a pattern of pits and lines on the head and down the flanks which appear to register movement and pressure in the water about them and thus afford valuable sensory aid to the swimming animal. Such organs are still present in the tadpole. They disappear, however, at metamorphosis and are absent in the adult frog; reptiles, too, have lost them, and they never reappear in higher vertebrate groups.

DIGESTIVE SYSTEM *

The mouth functions primarily as the anterior end of the digestive tract. Teeth are feeble and are confined to the upper jaws where there is a row along the jaw margins and a small patch on the front part of the palate. The tongue was noted in the discussion of frog habits. Mouth glands are poorly developed and merely secrete a mucous material; in contrast to man, they contain no digestive ferment. Beyond the mouth the alimentary canal passes back through the short pharynx, or throat region, and the distensible esophagus to reach the stomach. Pharynx and esophagus are lined with cilia, tiny hairlike structures, which, beating rhythmically, aid in passing food particles downward. The stomach is a simple pouch not dissimilar to that of man in shape and functions but rather less curved. It terminates at a construction, the pylorus ('gate-keeper'), where the food passes to the intestine.

The pancreas is rather diffuse in shape and lies along the course of the bile duct, into which its secretions pass to reach the intestine. The liver typically has two major lobes, left and

* Cf. pp. 314-24.

right; between them is a smaller lobe, while the gall bladder occupies a median position on the dorsal surface of the liver. The liver undergoes marked seasonal changes. In the summer it becomes large and light-coloured and is filled with glycogen and other food materials. During hibernation this food store is consumed, and the liver becomes a relatively small dark structure.

The small intestine of the frog has functions similar to that of man. It is relatively short, with but few coils. However, the tadpole, which eats vegetable rather than animal food, has a much longer intestine, coiled like a watch-spring. The large intestine is a short straight structure; there is no caecum or appendix. Its narrower, distal portion, the rectum, opens out into the cloaca, a

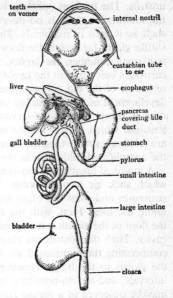

The digestive system of the frog seen from the ventral side. At the front the lower jaw has been cut away to expose the roof of the mouth. Much of the liver has been cut away and the remainder represented as pushed upward to expose the gall bladder and ducts. (Modified from Weidersheim)

pocket into which urinary and genital products also empty. The cloaca is a structure common to most lower vertebrates but absent in man and most mammals, where the intestine opens separately to the surface. The outer opening of the cloaca can be closed by a sphincter muscle.

RESPIRATORY SYSTEM *

The adult frog is an air-breather and a possessor of lungs. But even in the adult there are accessory breathing structures, while the tadpole is a water-dwelling user of gills.

Air in passage to the lungs enters the mouth through the

* Cf. pp. 324-9.

nostrils. The internal openings (choanae) are near the front of the mouth, for there is no development of a secondary palate such as is seen in mammals. The entrance to the lungs is the slitlike glottis far back in the floor of the mouth. Below the glottis is a small chamber, the larynx, which is partially enclosed by cartilages belonging to the hyoid apparatus; these cartilages are remnants of the old gill-bar system of the fish. The frog has no development of a long trachea such as is found in man, for the neck is short; beyond the larynx the air tube divides into two passages which almost immediately arrive at the lungs. These are relatively simple (and hence relatively inefficient) sacs lacking the complicated folds seen in the human lung.

A mammal breathes by movements of the ribs and diaphragm, which suck air into the lungs. The frog lacks both of these structures and must use other methods. There are two steps in filling the lung. First, with the mouth shut and nostrils open, the floor of the mouth is depressed. This sucks air into the mouth cavity. Then the nostrils are closed and the mouth floor raised, compressing the imprisoned air, which is thus pumped through the glottis to the lungs. However, the lungs are filled only at intervals, and mouth-breathing is a more frequent practice. As may be observed in a resting frog, the floor of the mouth rises and falls in a gentle, regular rhythm. Every now and then there is a more violent movement, indicating the filling of the lungs. The rest of the time there is merely a flow of air in and out of the mouth cavity. This orifice is lined with moist skin and acts as a breathing organ.

Still further, the skin of the frog is a moist and usually soft membrane. It can and does function in breathing and is richly supplied with blood vessels which utilize its potentialities as a respiratory organ. It has been found by careful measurement that even under normal conditions more carbon dioxide is given off by the frog's skin than by the lungs; and a frog submerged in cool water can obtain enough oxygen through the skin to live for several days.

Most vertebrates, apart from birds and mammals, are voiceless; the frogs, however, have evolved a pair of vocal cords which are fairly comparable to those of man and consist of a pair of elastic bands running across the larynx. Sounds are produced by the passage of air over these cords. In many frog species the males possess vocal sacs on either side of the throat which open into the floor of the back part of the mouth. These serve as resonators to reinforce the sounds produced by the cords.

EXCRETORY SYSTEM *

In both frog and man the basis of the excretory system consists of numbers of tiny tubules which filter from the blood water and waste matters, which are excreted as urine. These tubules are essentially the same in both animals, although (as discussed in the treatment of the human excretory system) the frog tubule carries a more dilute product. The mass of tissue containing the thousands of tubules constitutes the kidney. Despite the fundamental similarity of the units composing this structure, frog and man differ markedly in the shape and position of the kidneys and the drains passing the urine to the surface.

In the frog the kidneys form a pair of oval strips of dark-red tissue imbedded in the back wall of the body cavity. In man the kidney is much shortened and thickened to form a large bean-shaped structure, more posteriorly placed. In the frog the urine passes into a duct (technically known as the Wolffian duct) which, in the male, also carries the sperm from the testis. In man this tube, as noted elsewhere, has been given over to reproductive functions exclusively, and the urine leaves the kidney through a newly developed duct termed the ureter. This name is sometimes applied to the functional kidney duct of the frog, but improperly so, for the two are not at all homologous. In the frog the urine-carrying ducts pass directly to the cloaca, and a bilobed bladder for urine storage is found in the floor of the cloacal pouch. In man, on the other hand, the urinary bladder is more internally situated, and the two ducts lead directly to it.

REPRODUCTORY ORGANS †

FEMALE STRUCTURES. In the female frog the ovaries, the primary sex organs, are paired, more or less lobulate bodies lying in the dorsal part of the body cavity. They undergo great seasonal changes. When breeding is over in the spring they are reduced to tiny wrinkled bodies. During the summer they increase in size and by autumn may fill much of the abdomen.

* Cf. pp. 329–32.   † Cf. pp. 332–6.

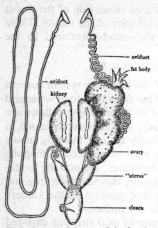

With the coming of the breeding season, the numerous eggs, which have been maturing meanwhile, burst out of the ovaries to fill the body cavity.

From this cavity the eggs pass to the surface through the oviducts, which also vary greatly from season to season and are much enlarged at breeding time. These tubes run most of the length of the abdomen. Anteriorly, near the base of the lung, is a wide, funnel-shaped mouth into which the eggs pass from the body cavity. Much of the length of the tube is highly convoluted. The inner surface of the duct is much wrinkled at breeding time. The ridges are covered with ciliated cells which are instrumental in passing the eggs down the duct. Between the folds are glands which secrete a gelatinous material to coat the egg. Near the exit to the cloaca there is a thin-walled portion of each tube, termed the 'uterus'. In these the eggs collect

The urinogenital organs of the female frog seen from the ventral aspect (semidiagrammatic). The urinary structures are similar to those of the male, but the sex products do not utilize the urinary duct; instead they pass through the highly coiled oviduct (which may be present in rudimentary form in the male also). On the left side of the figure the ovary has been removed and the oviduct artificially straightened to show its true length. The genital system is shown in a quiescent stage; as the reproductive period approaches the ovaries grow enormously, and subsequently the 'uteri' are distended with eggs.

before they are extruded, and the uteri may become greatly distended. These structures are not, of course, particularly comparable to the true uteri of mammals, in which development of the young takes place.

The oviduct does not function in the male, but in some species of frogs, including the leopard frog, it is present in a rudimentary state, lying lateral to the kidney duct. This is illustrative of the fact that in early development the typical vertebrate does not, so to speak, 'know' which sex it is destined to be, and the beginnings of the typical organs of both sexes may be present. Later in development the organs of one sex or the other dominate;

those of the opposite sex may disappear but may (as in this case) persist in a rudimentary, non-functional state.

MALE ORGANS. The primary sex organs of the male, the testes, are rounded bodies lying ventral to the kidneys and bound by membranes to the dorsal lining of the body cavity. The frog lacks the coiled epididymis which in mammals adjoins the testis. Instead, a number of efferent ducts pass across into the front part of the kidney. Crossing this structure, the sperm at breeding season pass down to the cloaca through the Wolffian duct, which, as noted above, also carries the urine. This situation, in which the testes 'impose on' the

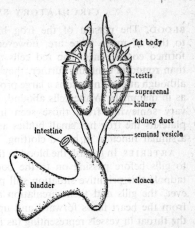

The urinogenital organs of the male frog seen from the ventral surface (semidiagrammatic). The testes have been pushed slightly laterally to show the slender vessels passing from them into the medial side of the kidneys. The suprarenals are thin masses of tissue lying on the ventral surface of the kidneys. The kidney ducts (also termed mesonephric or Wolffian ducts) drain not only the kidneys but the testes as well. The reproductive system is represented as in a quiescent stage. At the time of sexual activity the testis is enlarged, and the seminal vesicle may be greatly distended with sperm.

kidneys to obtain an outlet, is apparently a fairly primitive vertebrate condition. In mammals, the two types of products follow separate courses most of the way to the exterior. This is accomplished through the kidney evolving a new duct (ureter) for its exclusive use and politely turning the older structure over to the reproductive system as the sperm duct (ductus deferens). The front part of the kidney has been abandoned to help form the epididymis.

In both sexes we find, just in front of the gonads, a large yellowish organ, the fat body, with branching finger-like processes. This body serves as a storehouse for nutriment, waxing large in the summer and decreasing in size during the breeding season ; apparently the stored-up nutritive material is used by the sex organs.

CIRCULATORY SYSTEM *

BLOOD. The plasma of the frog blood is essentially similar to that of man; there are, however, some differences in the formed constituents. The red cells are larger and oval rather than round in contour; further, they tend to retain the nucleus, although at certain seasons a large proportion may be enucleated, as in mammals. White cells abound, although the types present vary somewhat from those seen in man. Instead of blood platelets the frog has small bodies as spindle cells, which have a similar function in blood clotting.

ARTERIES. In the fish the blood in the arteries flows from heart to gills before passing on to the body capillaries. In the frog tadpole this primitive situation still persists. In the adult, however, the gills and their circulation are eliminated. The blood from the heart flows forward and upward around the sides of the throat in vessels representing (as in man) three of the paired channels which in fishes lay between the gill slits.

The principal types of blood cells in the leopard frog. *A*, a normal red blood cell (erythrocyte). *B – D*, white blood corpuscles; *B*, a small lymphocyte; *C*, a large white cell filled with granules taking acid stains; *D*, a large white cell with subdivided ('polymorphic') nucleus. *E*, a spindle cell, associated with blood clotting. (From Noble, after Jordan)

Most anterior of these channels are the carotid arches, which carry blood to the head. Behind them are a pair of much larger vessels, which carry the blood to all parts of the trunk and limbs. These are the aortic arches. They run back above the body cavity and fuse to form a large median vessel, the dorsal aorta, which runs back close to the backbone. A notable difference between frog and man is that the frog preserves both members of the pair while in man that of the right side has been abandoned, and the dorsal aorta is continuous with the left arch. Most posterior of the arteries arising from the heart are those which lead to the lungs. These are also present in man as the pulmonary

* Cf. pp. 336–45.

arteries. In the human condition they emerge separately from the heart; in the frog, however, no such separation occurs.

VEINS. Into the frog heart empty veins carrying blood from the body organs. A pair of pulmonary veins drains the lungs.

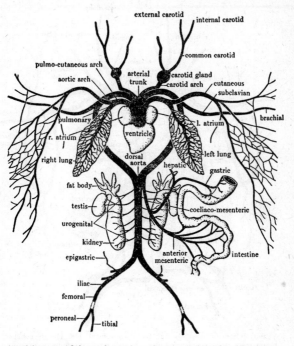

Arterial system of the toad seen from the ventral side. The blood leaves the heart through three pairs of channels. The most posterior (pulmo-cutaneous arches), which are mainly filled by deoxygenated blood from the body, pass to the lungs and to the skin (which is an accessory breathing structure). The main aortic arches carry blood to the body and limbs: the most anterior (carotids) supply the head. (After Jammes)

Two large vessels, anterior cardinals or venae cavae, bring blood from the head, front legs, and skin. These are compared with the superior vena cava of man, which has similar functions but has become a single rather than a paired structure. From the back part of the body comes the posterior vena cava, draining kidneys and liver. This large vein is closely comparable with the inferior vena cava of man, the shift in name being, of course, related to the changed posture of the body.

Blood from the leg and gut, however, does not pass directly to the heart; instead, the veins from these regions lead to capillary

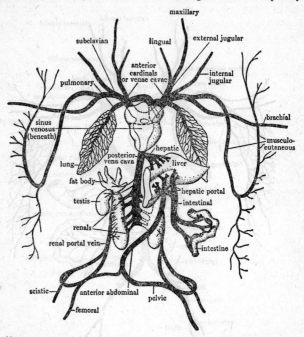

Venous system of the toad seen from the ventral side. The oxygenated blood from the lungs reaches the left atrium via the pulmonary veins. All other blood enters the right atrium by way of the sinus venosus (lying behind the heart and shown in broken lines). Three main channels enter the sinus: paired anterior cardinal veins (or venae cavae) and a single posterior vena cava. Blood from the hind legs may pass through the kidney (renal portal system) before reaching the posterior vena cava; blood from the intestine and some from the hind legs passes through the liver (hepatic portal system). (After Jammes)

systems in other organs – liver and kidneys – through which they drain before entering the main venous circulation. Such systems of veins are termed portal systems. One, the hepatic portal system, present in man as well as in frog, receives blood from the gut and sends it to the liver, where part of the food content may be stored. In the frog this system also receives part of the blood from the hind legs via a vein along the abdomen. In the frog we find also a renal portal system not present in the human circulation. This receives the remaining blood from the legs and sends it to circulate in the kidneys, thus assuring a sufficient flow of blood in those organs.

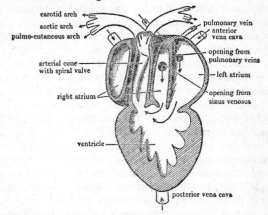

The heart of the frog as seen in diagrammatic section from the ventral surface. Blood from the lungs enters the left atrium through the pulmonary veins and thence passes to the ventricle. Deoxygenated blood from the body first passes via the venae cavae into the sinus venosus, which lies on the dorsal surface of the heart and is not seen in this figure. Thence it enters the right atrium (which is exposed in the figure on either side of the arterial cone) and from this chamber into the ventricle. From the ventricle the blood passes upward in the conus arteriosus. A spiral valve here assists in sorting out fresh and deoxygenated blood so that the latter tends to enter the pulmo-cutaneous arch, while the fresh blood tends to pass to the carotid and aortic arches.

HEART. In the typical fish the heart is a simple structure with simple functions. In it is received, in a single stream, the blood from all the organs. This is 'spent' blood, deprived of its oxygen in its passage through the body, and thus all of it is ready to pass to the breathing organs, the gills, to receive a new supply of that necessary element. We find, thus, that the fish heart is basically a single-tube structure pumping all the blood it receives forward in a single stream to the gills.

In lung-breathers, however, a major complication arises. Two blood streams are present. Fresh blood from the lungs should pass to the major body structures, while spent blood from the body should be pumped to the lungs. In man and other mammals this 'problem' has been adequately solved. Both major parts of the heart – atrium (or auricle) and ventricle – have been divided down the middle, a double-barrelled pump has been created, and the two blood streams are completely separated, although passing simultaneously through the one organ. In the frog the problem is, so to speak, in process of solution. The heart is incompletely divided; but, nevertheless, the two streams are fairly well separated.

The atrium, single in the fish, here consists of two chambers. The spent blood from the body first enters a thin-walled sac, the sinus venosus, on the upper surface of the heart and thence passes to the right atrium. The fresh blood from the heart, on the other hand, passes into the left atrium. The two blood streams thus enter the heart separately.

Beyond this point, however, structural separation does not occur. The ventricle is a single structure and so is a final region, the conus arteriosus, out of which lead all the major arteries. It would seem that the two streams would become hopelessly mixed in their further passage through the heart.

But, in fact, little mixture does take place. It will be noted that the right atrium opens into the ventricle farther forward than the left. When the atria contract, this topographic situation results in a ventricle filled with blood of both sorts but with the spent blood in advance of that from the lungs. Beyond the ventricle the arterial cone contains a peculiar spiral valve which tends to direct blood more readily to the pulmonary arteries than to the other sets of vessels. When the ventricle contracts, the spent blood thus tends properly to pass to the lungs; the blood behind, fresh from the lungs, finds the passages leading back to those structures full and hence flows, as it should, to the arches reaching body and head. The frog system of separation of blood streams seems a poor makeshift; but it works fairly effectively.

LYMPHATICS. Except for the thoracic duct, lymph circulation is relatively unimportant in man and other mammals. In the frog, however, the lymphatics are numerous. They mostly occur in the form of large, thin-walled sacs of irregular shape, between which there is a sluggish flow of liquid. A lymphatic cistern' of this sort occupies a large area above the walls of the body cavity and below the backbone; still more important is a whole series of lymph spaces which lie beneath the skin. Circulation of this liquid is brought about through the presence of two pairs of small pumping structures, the lymph hearts. One pair lies at the sides of the third segment of the backbone; the other pair is near the tip of the tail bone. They pulsate regularly and drain the lymph into the adjacent veins.

GLANDS OF INTERNAL SECRETION *

In the frog are present essentially the same glandular structures which form internal secretions in man, and the hormones formed in them appear to be in general of a similar nature. Since, however, much of the work on endocrines in recent decades has been done from the point of view of medicine and human biology, our knowledge of amphibian secretions is not so complete.

We have noted the presence of a well-developed pituitary in the frog. Here, as in man, this gland is of great importance not only in its direct effects but also through its influence on other endocrines. An interesting item to the biologist lies in its influence on the gonads. Many biological problems are studied through investigation on amphibian eggs and larvae. It was formerly necessary to wait until the spring breeding season to obtain eggs for such work. Now it has been discovered an extra 'shot' of pituitary extract may cause the laying of frogs' eggs at almost any season desired. The pituitary also has an influence on the coloration of frogs. If it is removed the darkly pigmented cells of the skin contract, and the frog becomes pallid; injections of pituitary extract restore the normal colour.

The frog thyroid is similar in function to that of man but differs in that it consists of two separate lobes. Since the thyroid is concerned with metabolism, it is but natural that it has been found to be of great importance at metamorphosis – a time at which the metabolic rate is very high. If thyroid extract is fed to immature tadpoles, they change promptly into tiny adults. If, on the other hand, the thyroid be removed from a young tadpole, it may continue to grow and may even reach sexual maturity but never change from the tadpole body form.

* Cf. pp. 345–52.

A number of small structures arise from the margins of the gill pouches in frogs, as in man. Little, however, is known of the possible functions of these bodies. The pancreas contains islands which are presumably a source of insulin. Frogs have tissues comparable to those which form both portions of the mammalian adrenal organs. They are, however, different in position and arrangement. The frog adrenals consist of bands of yellowish tissue extending along the undersides of the kidneys. In these bands are mixed masses of cells corresponding to the cortical and medullary portions of the mammalian organ. The sex glands too appear to form internal secretions similar to those of mammals; but, since reproductive functions are simpler in the frog, these secretions naturally are more restricted in their effects.

SKELETON AND MUSCLES *

It is in the skeletal system that we find the most marked specializations of the frog. The hopping gait is obviously responsible for the peculiar construction of the legs and limb girdles and undoubtedly has had much to do with the great shortening of the body. Even the skull is rather specialized and degenerate. Except for the expanded braincase, the human skeleton, 'advanced' as we think it to be, has a better claim to be regarded as primitive than has that of the frog, The study of the frog skeleton is not without interest; but we must not delude ourselves into believing that we are dealing with a 'generalized' structure.

The muscles too are highly specialized in many ways, particularly those of the limbs. In the course of study of the frog there is frequently included a dissection of some part of the musculature, such as the thigh. This is of use as an introduction to the methods of muscle dissection but is not to be regarded as of importance for purposes of comparative study. The muscles of this region form a complex system. To them are given names such as 'satorius', 'gracilis', etc., which suggest that we are dealing with the muscles known by the same terms in man. Comparative studies, however, show that for the most part this is not the case. The primitive land animal, with a clumsy gait, appears to have had but a small number of relatively massive muscles in its limbs. Both frog and man have become

* Cf. pp. 353-74.

agile types in which these muscle masses have eventually become subdivided into an intricate system. But the subdivisions have taken place independently in the two types, and there are few instances in which we can be sure that frog and human leg muscles are actually identical.

Both cartilage and bone are present in the frog; cartilage is rather more common, however, in the amphibian than in man. Much of the skull fails to ossify. In the limbs of mammals, as we have noted, the terminal portions form separate bony epiphyses, with 'growing points' of cartilage between them and the shaft. In the amphibians there are no such structures, and the ends of the bones frequently remain in a cartilaginous condition.

TRUNK SKELETON. In the frog the length of the body and, in consequence, the number of segments in the backbone are much reduced. In a majority of vertebrates (although not in man and his ape relatives) there is a long tail containing half-a-hundred or more vertebrae in many cases. In the frog the tail no longer projects beyond the body contours, and of the tail vertebrae there remains only a spike-like structure termed the urostyle, or 'tail pillar'.

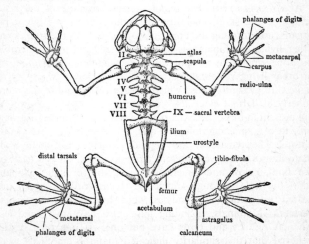

Skeleton of a common toad. Except in minor details, this is identical with the frog skeleton. (After Jammes)

Equally remarkable is the reduction in the more anterior part of the vertebral column. In most land forms the neck and trunk together contain about two dozen vertebrae, frequently more. In a typical frog there are only nine. A typical vertebra consists of two parts, neural arch and centrum, although the two ossify in the frog as a single bone. The arch encloses the spinal cord, extends upward as a neural spine, and sends out on either side an elongate transverse process. Both anterior and posterior margins of the arch bear a pair of processes termed zygapophyses, by means of which the successive vertebrae articulate with one another. The articular surfaces on the anterior zygapophyses face upward and inward, the posterior ones downward and outward. The centrum is oval in section, concave in front, and convex behind, each centrum receiving the projecting posterior end of the one ahead. The first vertebra has, anteriorly, a pair of concave oval surfaces which articulate with the skull; the last of the series, termed the sacral vertebra, has unusually heavy, transverse processes which connect with the pelvic girdle. In nearly all vertebrates ribs are present articulating with trunk vertebrae; the frogs are notable for the entire absence of these structures.

HEAD SKELETON. The major skeletal structure of the head region is the skull, enclosing the brain, sheltering the sense organs, and forming the upper jaws. The skull in the frog, as in other living amphibians, is much flattened, and a considerable portion remains in an embryonic cartilaginous condition. As in other living vertebrates above the shark level, two types of bones are present – those which replace cartilage and the more superficial dermal elements. Few replacement bones, however, are present in this degenerate type; of bones seen in the diagrams only three – sphenethmoid, pro-otic, and exoccipital – are of this nature. The remainder are dermal elements. But here, too, many bones primitively present have been lost. At the back of the skull, below and on either side of the foramen magnum (the 'big hole' through which the spinal cord emerges), are paired projections, the condyles, which articulate with the first vertebra. Mammals, including man, also have two condyles, whereas reptiles and birds have but one. At one time it was believed that this similarity indicated that the mammals were direct descendants of the amphibians. This, however, proves

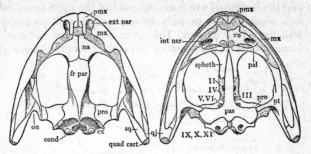

The skull of the bullfrog seen from dorsal and ventral surfaces. Cartilaginous areas are stippled. Certain of the nerve exits are marked in Roman numerals. *cond*, occipital condyle; *ex*, exoccipital; *ext nar*, external nares; *fr par*, fused frontal and parietal bones; *int nar*, internal nares; *mx*, maxilla; *na*, nasal; *on*, otic notch partially surrounding ear-drum; *pal*, palatine; *pas*, parasphenoid; *pmx*, premaxilla; *pro*, pro-otic; *pt*, pterygoid; *qj*, quadratojugal; *quad cart*, quadrate cartilage; *spheth*, sphenethmoid; *sq*, squamosal; *vo*, vomer.

not to be the case, for we now know that early amphibians had only one condyle; the frog and mammal have in this regard merely evolved in parallel fashion.

Whereas the human jaw consists of but a single bone, that of the frog contains three bony elements of the ten or so primitively present in land vertebrates. In the throat region between the jaws lies a series of cartilages known collectively as the hyoid apparatus; they are the remains of the bars which in fish stiffened the gill arches.

GIRDLE AND LIMB SKELETON. In the bones of the appendages and the girdles which support them, the frog exhibits most of the elements found in all typical land vertebrates but in a rather specialized condition correlated with leaping habits.

The pectoral or chest girdle, supporting the front legs, includes as a main dorsal element the scapula, corresponding to the human shoulder blade; above is a feebly ossified extension termed the suprascapula. Below the arm socket a bone extending downward and backward is called the coracoid (the human bone of this name is a mere nubbin). Directly down below the front of the scapula is the clavicle, the equivalent of the human collarbone. In the ventral midline is a fore-and-aft series of bones and cartilages which forms the sternum.

The pelvic girdle includes a more or less circular structure into the middle of which fits the head of the thigh bone, and a long process which projects upward and forward to articulate with the sacral vertebra. The upper bone of the girdle is the ilium; a bone at the posterior end is the ischium. Besides these

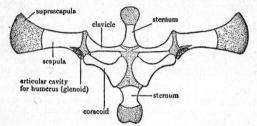

Shoulder girdle of the frog seen spread out in ventral view. Except for the clavicle (collarbone), the elements are preformed in cartilage, and considerable cartilage may remain even in the adult. The major elements of the girdle are scapula and coracoid. In the centre are elements of the sternum, which pertains to the axial skeleton rather than the shoulder girdle.

two elements the human pelvic girdle includes a third, the pubis; in the frog (as in many amphibians) this bone tends to remain unossified.

In the front leg the first segment contains in normal fashion a single element, the humerus. Beyond the elbow a typical vertebrate exhibits two bones, radius and ulna; in the frog these are fused into one. The wrist, or carpus, contains half-a-dozen small elements; beyond are the metacarpals and phalanges making up the toes. Four toes are typically developed, although short; an inner spur, sometimes regarded as the missing 'thumb', is probably not of this nature (it may be much enlarged in the breeding male, serving as a clasper).

The long hind leg begins proximally with a characteristic femur, or thigh bone. But the second segment (as in the front leg)

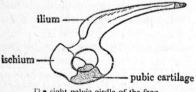

The right pelvic girdle of the frog. The pubis remains unossified.

consists of a single bone, regarded as a fusion of the tibia and fibula normally present. Beyond lies the tarsus, or ankle bones. Here is still another peculiarity of the frog.

Typically, the tarsal bones (like those of the wrist) are tiny structures. In the frog, however, two proximal elements (astragalus, calcaneum) are much elongated. This development has the result of adding a third segment to the hind leg and greatly increasing its effectiveness in hopping. Five toes are present in the hind foot.

LIFE-HISTORY

The development of the common species of frog takes place in a water environment, the streams or ponds in which the eggs are deposited in the spring breeding season. The egg contains a modest supply of nutrient yolk and furnishes a food supply for the embryo during the stages in which the major body structures and the tadpole body shape are acquired. Hatching soon occurs, however, and the larva, hardly larger than a pin, must seek its own living. The tadpole is, of course, markedly different from the adult both in general appearance and in many structural features. There is a powerful tail, used as a swimming organ; limbs, on the other hand, are absent until a late period. Lungs are not developed, and breathing is accomplished by means of gills. The adult frog is an eater of animal food, but the tadpole, on the contrary, feeds on vegetable material. In relation to this we find many differences in the mouth and jaws between tadpole and adult, and even the intestine is built on a different plan.

The period of tadpole existence is of variable length in frogs. In some species the entire development takes place in a few weeks; on the other hand, the bullfrog spends several years in the tadpole stage. Eventually, in any case, comes the period of metamorphosis, the change of bodily shape which turns tadpole into frog. This process involves a marked reorganization of almost every part of the animal's body. The tail is resorbed; the limbs grow out (the hind legs appearing first), the gills disappear, and lungs develop; the long, spirally-coiled tadpole intestine changes into the relatively short adult structure; many head structures are radically reorganized.

These changes accomplished, the frog becomes a potential land dweller. With further development in size and proportions and the growth of the sex organs, the frog, by the time of the breeding season of the next spring, has arrived at maturity.

CHAPTER 5

The Origin of Reptiles

IN contrast with the conservative mode of development of the amphibians is that of the reptiles and the higher tetrapods derived from them. The reptile has evolved a type of egg which can be laid on land. No aquatic life-stage is necessary; emancipation from the water is complete.

THE LAND EGG. This reptilian egg has a complicated structure to which we must devote some attention, for many of the architectural features first attained here are still persistent in the wrappings of the human embryo.

The developing amphibian obtains its oxygen and most of its food from the water and excretes its waste matter into the water again; the water also protects it from drying and against mechanical injury. In the reptile, if the water-dwelling stage is to be omitted, substitutes must be provided for these advantages which will carry the youngster through to a stage where it can make its own way on land.

As a food supply for the embryo, the egg of a reptile or bird contains a large amount of nourishing yellow yolk which, as the embryo grows, is contained in a sac connected with the digestive tract. A large sac, the amnion, develops about the body of the embryo. This liquid-filled sac affords protection against injury and desiccation; it is a substitute for the amphibian's natal pond. Out from the back end of the embryo's body there grows a tube and sac, the allantois, in which the waste matter of the body is deposited. The whole egg structure is stiffened and protected by a firm shell on the exterior. The shell, however, is porous; beneath a portion of it lies a membrane pertaining to the allantois, richly supplied with blood vessels. This acts as a lung, taking in oxygen and giving off carbon dioxide; and it is an easily confirmed fact that a reptile or bird egg if submerged in water will drown as surely as an adult; the contained embryo ceases to grow, and dies.

By these structures – yolk sac, amnion, allantois, and shell – all the needs of the developing reptile can be cared for; the need for a water-dwelling stage is eliminated, and the embryo can develop directly – and more perfectly – towards a purely land existence, which it assumes immediately upon hatching. We have here for the first time a true land form, completely emancipated from the water.

While the shift in type of development seems obviously the major advance of reptiles over amphibians, there have been other structural changes as well. Limbs and backbone, muscles, lungs, heart and blood vessels, kidneys, and many other structures have become better adapted to land life, and in the brain there is present the first trace of the higher centres in the cerebral hemispheres (the neopallium: cf. chap. 17) which were to play a major role in the mental evolution of the later mammals.

STEM REPTILES. Living reptiles include only a few groups, mainly turtles, crocodiles, lizards, and snakes; they are vastly overshadowed in importance to-day by the birds and mammals descended from them. In the Mesozoic, the Age of Reptiles, however, the reptiles were exceedingly numerous and varied and included many groups now extinct. These forms will be

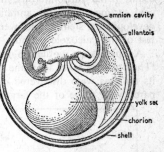

Generalized diagram of the embryonic membranes of the higher land vertebrates (amniotes). The developing embryo is surrounded, except ventrally, by a liquid-filled cavity which is enclosed by the amnion, a membrane continuous with the skin of the embryo. Developing from this and, as shown in the diagram, continuous with it at an early stage is a second membrane, the chorion, which lies beneath the shell. Two membranes grow out from the embryonic digestive tract; a yolk sac, directly below the embryo, is filled in reptiles and birds with a large mass of yolk; from the back end of the gut grows out the allantois, which can function as an embryonic bladder. Blood vessels surrounding it may carry to the embryo oxygen which has passed in through the porous shell of the egg in reptiles and birds, so that the allantois may function as an embryonic lung. In typical mammals the chorion comes into close contact with the surrounding maternal tissues to form a placenta whereby the embryo obtains nutriment from the mother; in such cases the blood vessels of the allantois carry the nutritive materials from placenta to embryo.

described in succeeding chapters; here we shall merely consider the earliest reptiles, first types to attain a land type of egg.

These extinct progenitors of the reptile dynasties are technically known as cotylosaurs but popularly and quite appropriately have been termed 'stem reptiles'. The first traces of them are found in the Carboniferous, in the deposits formed in the great coal swamps when the amphibians were at the peak of their development; stem reptiles were still flourishing in the Permian, last of the Paleozoic periods.

A typical stem reptile is *Seymouria*, shown in our illustrations. (The creature takes its name from the Texas town near which its remains were discovered.) In appearance it might be compared with some of the larger and more sluggish lizards; but

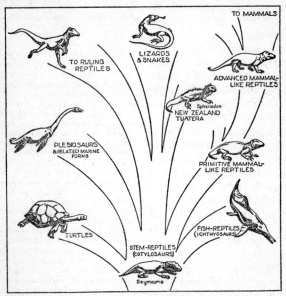

The family tree of the reptiles (except the archosaurs, ruling reptiles, shown elsewhere).

structurally it was much more primitive than any sort of lizard. The limbs were still of the short, stubby type found in the oldest amphibians and sprawled out sideways from the body. Indeed, so close is *Seymouria* in many skeletal features to the early amphibians that, in default of actual fossil knowledge of eggs of this form, the academic question has been raised as to whether *Seymouria* was an amphibian which was almost a reptile or, on the other hand, a reptile which had just ceased to be an amphibian. This debate, however, merely emphasizes the point that it is the change in development which is the important feature in the history of reptiles; without this, the great radiation of the group and the many structural advances and changes could never have been accomplished or effectively utilized.

During the Permian the stem reptiles branched out into a number of varied lines. But their fate has been that of the founders of any great line of evolutionary development; from them arose many more progressive groups, and they themselves soon vanished from the scene as the true Age of Reptiles began.

CHAPTER 6

Ruling Reptiles

ONCE the primitive reptiles had been freed from the restrictions of their ancestors' aquatic existence, there began a great radiation of the saurian types which were to dominate the earth during the hundred million years or more of history known as the Age of Reptiles, or Mesozoic era.

REPTILIAN LOCOMOTION

PRIMITIVE WALKERS. In no way is the great diversity of the numerous reptilian groups better shown than in their locomotor adaptations. The gait of the primitive land forms was an exceedingly clumsy one. The limbs were widely sprawled out at the sides of the body, the trackway broad, the step short, the walk a slow and waddling one. Such a type of walking is exhausting, for much muscular effort is needed merely to keep the body off the ground; the attainment of speed or the development of large size is impossible.

The turtles in their armour, oblivious to the world, have retained this old-fashioned mode of locomotion to the present day. The lizards have become somewhat slimmer-legged, four-footed types, but have not improved their limbs much and have amounted to comparatively little. The snakes, their cousins, have abandoned limbs altogether and evolved their own peculiar style of progression. Several reptilian groups have dodged the issue by returning to the water and reshaping legs into finlike structures.

Some reptiles, the forerunners of the mammals, remained four-limbed land dwellers but improved their method of walking, with important evolutionary results; in a later chapter we shall discuss these ancestors of ours which tucked their legs under their bodies and became efficient four-footed runners.

THE EVOLUTION OF BIPEDS. Here we shall tell the story of a second reptilian group in which better running powers were attained but attained in quite a different way – the story of the archosaurs, or ruling reptiles. To-day these forms are represented only by the crocodiles, a rather unprogressive and degenerate order; but the extinct dinosaurs and flying reptiles were also archosaurs, and the birds are descendants of this group. The ruling reptiles were the dominant forms on the land and in the sky during the Mesozoic, and the evolutionary story of the Age of Reptiles is in great measure one which tells of the rise and fall of the archosaurian dynasties.

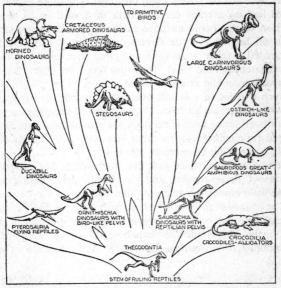

An outline of the phylogeny of the ruling reptiles. From the primitive stock came the crocodiles, flying reptiles, and the two great orders of dinosaurs, while the birds have also descended from this group.

Speedy locomotion in archosaurs was obtained by running not on all fours but on the hind limbs; among the ruling reptiles were the world's first bipeds. How this sort of process might have started may be seen among some lizards of to-day, such as the 'mountain boomer' of the south-west U.S.A. When great speed is necessary, the front end of the body is lifted from the ground and balanced by the long tail. The inefficient front feet are relieved from duty, and the better-developed hind legs carry the whole weight of the body swiftly forward until the burst of speed is over, and the four-footed posture is again assumed. None of the lizards has ever become a true biped; the ruling reptiles belong to a quite different stock but had a parallel early history.

PRIMITIVE RULING REPTILES

The ancestral archosaurs come into view in the Triassic, first of the Mesozoic periods. These progenitors of the dinosaurs and birds were comparatively small creatures. The more generalized types had an average overall length of a yard or so, a great portion of this being included in the long tail. In appearance such an animal as little *Ornithosuchus* would probably have resembled a fairly large modern lizard. Structurally, however, the differences were great. The front legs were short, the hind legs very long and much modified.

Such a creature was still able, when resting or progressing slowly, to walk on all fours. But when speed was necessary, the small front limbs were lifted from the ground, and speedy two-legged running became the order of the day, the weight of the tilted body being balanced by the long tail.

It is from such ancestors that there came the crocodiles, dinosaurs, flying reptiles, and birds; with the development of these little bipeds the ruling reptiles had begun their career.

The history of the group has not been a simple one. From this stock came not only the prominent groups mentioned above but many short side-line 'experiments' which were quickly abandoned. For example, during the Triassic some of these

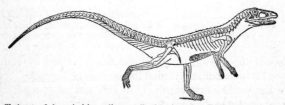

Skeleton of the primitive ruling reptile *Ornithosuchus*. This Triassic fossil reptile was about 3 feet long (tail included). (From Heilmann, *The Origin of Birds*, by permission of D. Appleton – Century Co., publishers)

primitive archosaurs tended to take to a water-dwelling life, abandoned the bipedal habits already begun, and, as phytosaurs became common Triassic animals, represented to-day by fossils from many parts of the world. These forms were quite similar to crocodiles in size and appearance and probable habits; for readier breathing while lying in the water the nostrils were sometimes situated in a 'crater' rising above the eyes.

Restoration of *Ornithosuchus*, a primitive ruling reptile. Although differing greatly in internal structure, such a dinosaur ancestor would have looked rather like a lizard. Probably when unhurried, this little reptile was still a four-footed walker. (From Heilmann, *The Origin of Birds*, by permission of D. Appleton – Century Co., publishers.)

CROCODILES

The crocodiles were fully evolved by the following (Jurassic) period and replaced the phytosaurs as water dwellers. The phytosaurs were not the ancestors but the 'uncles' of the crocodiles, which represent a parallel evolution from the primitive ruling reptile stock. The modern alligators, crocodiles, and gavials are a rather retrogressive group of ruling reptiles. These sluggish creatures have wandered far from the bipedal pathway which their early ancestors had taken, although they have still, one may note, the long hind legs and short front ones that are characteristic of the group. They alone of ruling reptiles, however, have survived, secure in their specialized position in the world, while their more ambitious reptilian cousins have had their splendid day and have gone.

The one conspicuous advance in crocodiles is their development of a false palate. The inner opening of the nostrils in a primitive land form lay in the front of the mouth. This is an

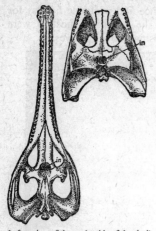

Left, a view of the underside of the skull of a Jurassic crocodile (*Steneosaurus*). The inner opening of the nostrils (*in*) lies far back towards the throat, although the external opening lay at the tip of the snout. *Right*, the back part of the palate of a modern type of crocodile; the internal nostril opening is almost at the back end of the skull.

awkward position for the nostrils in a long-snouted water dweller; the chances of shipping water while breathing are considerable. We have noted that the phytosaurs had moved the nostrils back over the top of the head and thus shortened the distance to the throat. In the crocodiles there is a much better breathing mechanism. The nostrils remain at the tip of the snout. But underneath this there has been erected a partition running the entire length of the roof of the mouth, separating off the air passages. With the aid of this bony secondary palate and a flap at the entrance to the throat the crocodile or alligator can breathe perfectly well under water with the mouth open, provided only that the tip of the nose is above the surface. This adaptation is peculiarly suitable to the mode of life of these forms.

While archosaurs were triumphant on the land and in the air, they tended little to invade the seas. Only one marine ruling reptile group ever entered salt water – marine crocodiles found in Jurassic deposits. These animals had turned their limbs into steering paddles and redeveloped a rather fishlike tail. They were, however, a short-lived group – successful invasion of the seas was reserved for members of other reptilian stocks.

FLYING REPTILES

With the adoption of the bipedal gait, the front legs of the archosaurs became freed for other uses. In some groups they tended to degenerate; in a few forms they functioned as grasping organs, 'hands'. In two cases they took on an entirely new use – that of wings, organs of flight. Flight was twice evolved in the ruling reptile stock; once by the ancestors of the birds, as noted later; again, and for the time more successfully, by the flying reptiles.

The pterosaurs ('winged reptiles'), or pterodactyls ('wing-fingered'), were common forms during the Jurassic, middle period of the Age of Reptiles. The remains of these and many other contemporary animals have been preserved in considerable numbers in German lithographic stone deposits such as that at Solenhofen. These deposits appear to represent fine sediments which settled in the bottom of ancient coral-reef lagoons, and in them are preserved many delicate structures such as jellyfishes and wing impressions of pterosaurs. A good example of a primitive

The skeleton of *Rhamphorhynchus*, a long-tailed Jurassic pterosaur. About one-fourth natural size. Impressions of the soft tissues of the tail 'rudder' and wing membranes are often preserved. The wings were supported by one very long and powerful finger (the fourth). The other fingers were short and, with the feeble hind legs, were probably used for clutching purposes when at rest. (From Williston, *The Osteology of the Reptiles*, by permission of the Harvard University Press)

flying reptile was *Rhamphorhynchus* (not a bad name to spell if sprinkled liberally with *h*'s), shown in our figures. This was a creature about a yard in length, with a long beak armed with sharp teeth, a short body, and a long tail tipped by a steering rudder. The hind legs were slim and feeble; but the front legs were powerful wing supports.

In the hand the first three fingers were short and armed with claws. The little finger had been lost. The fourth one, however, was very stout and long and was the sole support of the wing, a batlike flap of skin which ran back to the thigh region.

This type of flying structure is, of course, quite in contrast to that of birds. Nothing in the nature of feathers was present in the pterosaurs.

These aerial reptiles appear to have been fish-eating types, flying over the water and diving after small fishes much as do some modern marine birds. What they did when ashore to rest or nest, however, has been a disputed problem. The legs were ill suited for walking purposes but were perfectly good clutching organs, as were three fingers of the 'hand'. Probably, like the bats, they hung suspended from tree limbs or overhanging rocks during their times of rest.

Besides these long-tailed flying reptiles, the Jurassic lagoon deposits have also yielded remains of short-tailed relatives, some no bigger than a sparrow. These were destined (in contrast to the more primitive ruddered pterosaurs) to last over into the Cretaceous, the third and last of the great reptile periods. Some forms of this age grew to great size. *Pteranodon*, a form found in the chalk rocks deposited by the seas which once covered western Kansas, had a wingspread of twenty-seven feet in one specimen and was thus much larger than any bird. The beak was toothless; and a curious feature was an enormous crest projecting from the back of the head like a weather vane. *Pteranodon* and his kin were the last of flying reptiles. By that time birds were already far along in their developmental history and soon entirely superseded their reptilian cousins as aerial navigators.

DINOSAURS

The story of the dinosaurs is one of the most interesting of all the evolutionary sagas furnished by the vertebrates. Beginning in the Triassic, they increased greatly in numbers and size in the Jurassic and Cretaceous, ruled the earth without rivals for nearly the whole extent of the Mesozoic, and at its close disappeared for ever from the world.

We customarily think of the dinosaurs as a group of gigantic reptiles. This, however, is not quite the case. Among the dinosaurs were the largest animals that ever walked, but other dinosaurs were no bigger than chickens. Further, while all dinosaurs were descendants of the primitive ruling reptile stock, there were two quite separate groups of them, each containing a number of remarkable types.

THE TWO DINOSAUR STOCKS. These two groups are termed scientifically the Saurischia and Ornithischia, meaning 'reptile-like pelvis' and 'bird-like pelvis'. The pelvis, or hip bones, offers a fine key character for distinguishing between the two dinosaurian types, and we shall dwell for a moment on the technicalities of hip construction.

The hip bones of any land animal consist of three parts. Above the socket for the thigh bone is the ilium, fused to the backbone.

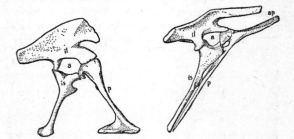

The right pelvic bones of dinosaurs, to show the contrast between the two great orders. *Left*, the triradiate pelvis of a reptile-like dinosaur (order SAURISCHIA). *Right*, the tetraradiate pelvis of a bird-like form (order ORNITHISCHIA). In each case the socket (*a*) for the thigh bone is bordered by three elements: the ilium above, the pubis below and towards the front, the ischium below and towards the back. In the bird-like form, however, the pubis is two-pronged, with an anterior process (*ap*).

Below the socket lie the pubis in front and the ischium behind. In primitive land dwellers these last two form a solid plate. In early ruling reptiles, however, the two have diverged considerably, the pubis slanting down in front, the ischium running down behind. This makes a three-pronged pelvis, each of the bones running off from the hip socket at a considerable angle to the others.

This type of construction, not so far from that of ordinary reptiles, still persisted in the saurischian, or reptile-like dinosaurs, including the flesh-eaters and the giant amphibious forms. In the other order, the Ornithischia, or bird-like dinosaurs (including among others the duck-billed dinosaurs and the armoured and horned types), there has been a further complication. The pubis has swung back parallel to the ischium, just as in the birds. But, as an aid to the support of the belly, a new bony process has grown forward from the base of the pubis, giving a characteristic four-pronged type of pelvis. This structure is, as we have said, similar to that found in birds; but it cannot be too strongly emphasized that the birds are not descended from these dinosaurs; the two groups are essentially 'cousins', descended separately from a common ancestor at the base of the ruling reptile stock.

FOOTPRINTS. Both dinosaur groups were already in existence before the end of the Triassic, and numerous footprints have been found of dinosaurs of this age in the rocks representing old mud flats of the Connecticut Valley region. These bring out

A restoration of dinosaur life on the shores of the Triassic waters of the modern Connecticut Valley region showing some of the dinosaur types which may have been responsible for the numerous footprints. (The artist, incidentally, was mistaken in restoring this as a body of salt water and with seaweed; it was actually a fresh-water deposit.) (From Heilmann, *The Origin of Birds*, by permission of D. Appleton – Century Co., publishers)

an interesting feature of dinosaur anatomy. In many dinosaurs with a bipedal gait the main reliance was placed on the three centre toes; the outer one was lost, and the inner one often turned back as a rear prop. In this arrangement we have an exact parallel, even to the number of joints and comparative length of toes, to the structure of the bird foot. These footprints were discovered over a century ago. At that time dinosaurs were almost unheard of, and the tracks were (not unnaturally) long thought to be those of gigantic birds!

SMALL CARNIVOROUS DINOSAURS. We shall first consider the history of the Saurischia, or reptile-like dinosaurs. These were already abundant in the late Triassic. The early forms were comparatively small, swift, flesh-eating bipeds, as were some of

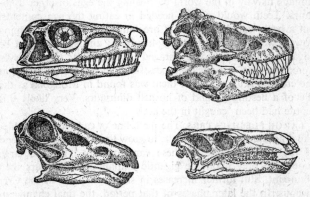

The skulls of some ruling reptiles to show the similarity of the pattern in the group and some of the modifications. *Upper left*, a small ancestral member of the group (*Euparkeria*). *Upper right*, the giant carnivorous dinosaur *Tyrannosaurus*; a large skull with huge sharp teeth suitable for a flesh-eater. *Lower left*, *Diplodocus*, an amphibious plant-eater, with a feeble dentition. *Lower right*, *Stegosaurus*, a bird-like dinosaur, a herbivore with a toothless bill and cheek teeth somewhat adapted for chewing.

the stem archosaurs mentioned previously; little change was needed to turn one of these old forms into a primitive reptile-like dinosaur. Bipedal flesh-eaters continued to be the main stock of the saurischians throughout their history, and many of them long kept to a small size. The small form *Compsognathus*, for example, shown in our illustration of the Solenhofen lagoon, was no larger than a rooster. This little type presumably preyed upon small reptiles of the lizard sort and perhaps even upon our own relatives, the tiny early mammals which were already in existence.

An interesting end development of these comparatively small and lightly built members of the carnivorous group is that exemplified by the Cretaceous 'ostrich dinosaur' *Struthiomimus* and its kin. These were somewhat larger in size, with rather ostrich-like proportions, except for the development of the tail and front limbs. They were toothless, presumably having a horny, bird-like bill; the hind legs show evidences of fast-running abilities; the three-fingered hands evidently had considerable grasping powers. The probable habits of this creature have been a subject of considerable debate. It was finally suggested that it made its way in the world by stealing the eggs of other dinosaurs. Teeth would not be needed in eating the egg contents, but a beak would be useful in breaking the shell. The grasping powers would be useful in egg-handling; and speed would be advantageous in avoiding enraged parents. That these thieves were, however, not always successful is shown by the fact that the crushed skull of one of them was found in Mongolia at the site of a nesting ground of horned dinosaurs. Very likely this reptile had been 'caught in the act'.

LARGE FLESH-EATERS. The main line of carnivorous reptile-like dinosaurs tended, however, to grow to large size. By the end of the Jurassic some of these carnivores had become large enough to prey upon the gigantic amphibious dinosaurs then abundant. Still further increases in size took place in the Cretaceous. In the later phases of that period, the final chapter in dinosaur history, we find huge bipeds of the type of *Tyrannosaurus*, the 'tyrant reptile'. This great flesh-eater, the largest carnivore that ever walked the earth, stood some nineteen feet in height. The hind legs were very powerful; the front ones, however, had degenerated so that they were not even able to reach the mouth, much less be useful in walking, and had retained but two feeble fingers. The skull was a massive structure more than four feet in length, armed with numerous sabre-like teeth that must have been highly effective biting and rending weapons.

AMPHIBIOUS DINOSAURS. But in the late Triassic some of the reptile-like dinosaurs, which were already tending to quite large size, seem from their teeth to have been changing to a plant diet and (in correlation with their considerable bulk and lessened need for speed, as plant-eaters) appear to have been slumping back into a four-footed method of walking.

From such beginnings came the great amphibious dinosaurs, the sauropods, the largest four-footed creatures that ever existed. They were present throughout the Jurassic and Cretaceous but seem to have reached the peak of their development at the end of the former period. Numerous remains of amphibious dinosaurs of that age have been quarried in the western U.S.A., and one such deposit (at Jensen, Utah) has been preserved as a national monument.

Brontosaurus and *Diplodocus* are among these large creatures whose remains form a major attraction of many museums.

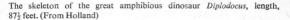

The skeleton of the great amphibious dinosaur *Diplodocus*, length, 87½ feet. (From Holland)

Diplodocus, at eighty-seven and a half feet, holds the length record but was rather slimly built and was far from the heaviest. Twenty-five to thirty-five tons is a fair estimate of the weight of an average full-sized member of the group. In all these forms we find a massively built body, powerful limbs with a four-footed pose (but the front legs usually much shorter than the hind), a long tail, and a long neck terminating in a small head.

The head seems absurdly out of proportion to the body. The eyes were high up on the sides and the nostrils sometimes at the very top of the skull above them. This position is like that of the 'blow-hole' in whales and is one of the reasons for believing that these giant reptiles were amphibious in their habits, spending much of their lives in the water; the animal could breathe and see with only the top of the head exposed above the surface.

The jaws were short and weak, the teeth feeble and few in number. It seems almost incredible that such a feeding apparatus could have gathered enough material to supply the huge body. although the fodder may have been some soft type of water vegetation which could be cropped with little effort. The brain is small in all reptiles but excessively small in these dinosaurs in proportion to their size. Very likely the brain did little except work the jaws, receive impressions from the sense organs, and pass the news along down the spinal cord to the hip region, from which came the nerves working the hind legs. Between the hips there was situated an enlargement of the cord several times the size of the brain.

This condition inspired the following flight of fancy on the part of the late Bert L. Taylor, a columnist on the staff of the *Chicago Tribune:*

> Behold the mighty dinosaur,
> Famous in pre-historic lore,
> Not only for his power and strength
> But for his intellectual length.
> You will observe by these remains
> The creature had two sets of brains –
> One in his head (the usual place),
> The other at his spinal base.
> Thus he could reason *a priori*
> As well as *a posteriori*.
> No problem bothered him a bit;
> He made both head and tail of it.
> So wise was he, so wise and solemn,
> Each thought filled just a spinal column.
> If one brain found the pressure strong
> It passed a few ideas along.
> If something slipped his forward mind
> 'Twas rescued by the one behind.
> And if in error he was caught
> He had a saving afterthought.
> As he thought twice before he spoke
> He had no judgement to revoke.
> Thus he could think without congestion
> Upon both sides of every question.
> Oh, gaze upon this model beast,
> Defunct ten million years at least.

A monumental construction of the backbone was necessary to carry the tons of weight of the enormous body and to transfer it to the legs. Nature had solved the engineering problems involved in competent fashion. The backbone formed an arch, supported at the top by the massive hind legs beneath the stout hips and tapered away in each direction from this pier. The dead weight of the bone of the spinal column was a considerable burden in itself; this weight had been reduced by hollowing out the sides of the vertebrae, leaving only the essential framework of these bones.

The hind legs were very massive and appear to have been quite straight, weight-bearing columns like the limbs of elephants. The front legs, usually much shorter, and thus reminiscent of these animals' bipedal ancestors, bore less weight and may have been a bit crooked at the elbows. The feet seem to have been huge rounded pads with two or three large claws which would have been of aid on a slippery bottom.

Even with these stout legs it is difficult to see how these dinosaurs ever walked on land. The elements of physics show that there are natural limits set to the possible size of a four-footed land vertebrate. The weight of an animal varies in proportion to the cube of a linear dimension. But the strength of a leg, like any supporting element in engineering, is proportionate to its cross-section, which increases only by squares. If a reptile doubles his length, his weight is about eight times as great, but his legs are only four times as strong. Hence in large animals the bulk of the legs must increase out of all proportion to the rest of the body. An elephant does not and cannot have the slim legs of a gazelle; and in the case of these great dinosaurs it seems doubtful if their limbs, stout as they were, could have effectively supported so many tons on land. It thus appears probable that the sauropods were amphibious types which spent most of their lives in lowland swamps and lagoons where, buoyed up by the water, problems of support and locomotion were greatly simplified.

Brachiosaurus, the largest known dinosaur, with an estimated weight of about 50 tons and with a height great enough to look over the top of a three-storey building. This form is known from Jurassic deposits of both Wyoming and East Africa. (From Abel)

The giant of the group was Brachiosaurus. This form was first known from incomplete remains from the western United States, now in the Field Museum, Chicago. There was only enough material to show that the animal was a large one, with (exceptionally) long front legs. Later a skeleton of an apparently identical animal was discovered by Germans in East Africa and has been mounted in Berlin. This form was short-bodied, with a stub tail, but despite this may have reached a live weight of fifty tons. Above the long front legs there stretched up a long neck by means of which this dinosaur could easily have looked over the top of a three-storey building. This giant of giants was apparently capable of living in waters of considerable depth.

The amphibious dinosaurs reached a peak at the end of the Jurassic; they played only a small part in the Cretaceous act of the reptilian drama and then vanished.

BIRDLIKE DINOSAURS

The story of the reptile-like dinosaurs was paralleled by that of the ornithischians, which resembled their avian cousins in hip

A restoration of the primitive birdlike dinosaur, *Camptosaurus*. Shown here in a four-footed pose which was perhaps assumed when walking slowly; for fast travel the animal was undoubtedly a biped. (From Heilmann, *The Origin of Birds*, by permission of D. Appleton – Century Co., publishers)

structure and hence are called birdlike dinosaurs. It must, of course, be kept in mind that these forms were not bird ancestors and, except in this feature, did not resemble birds any more closely than did other ruling reptiles. (READER: 'You said that before.' AUTHOR: 'I know, but you had forgotten.' READER: 'Nothing of the sort.' AUTHOR: 'Very well then; let's get on with the story.')

PRIMITIVE HERBIVOROUS BIPEDS. These reptiles were rare in the Triassic but common in the two following periods. The early members of the group are well represented by *Camptosaurus*.

a Jurassic type which ranged from about eight to twenty feet in length in different species. The early birdlike dinosaurs were, like the primitive saurischians, bipedal in fast locomotion, but the front legs were usually comparatively little reduced, and these animals (as the figure suggests in the case of *Camptosaurus*) may well have strolled about on all fours when not particularly hurried.

A major difference between these birdlike forms and the other dinosaurs lies in the fact that all had abandoned a carnivorous life and were herbivores from the beginning. In connexion with this mode of life, almost all of them had lost their front teeth and replaced them, it would seem, by a stout, birdlike, horny beak. The teeth in the back of the jaws were no longer pointed but were leaflike chewing teeth with rough edges. What each tooth lacked in grinding power was often made up for by an increase in numbers; in some of the duckbills mentioned below there were somewhere between fifteen hundred and two thousand teeth in the mouth at one time.

DUCKBILLS. In the Cretaceous, bipedal birdlike forms were abundant. The prominent group was that of the duckbilled dinosaurs, or trachodonts. These were large forms, exceedingly numerous in the late Cretaceous of North America, and many skulls and skeletons are known. The name arises from the fact that there was a broad, ducklike beak. The limbs were massive, and probably they were far from speedy. In several cases there have been found 'mummies' of these duckbills. The dinosaur corpses had dried and hardened before being buried, and the surrounding mould of rock has caused the formation within it of a natural cast of the details of the skin. These mummies show that the duckbills had webbed feet and presumably were amphibious in habits, feeding in swampy pools or about their margins.

A curious event in duckbill history was the development of crested types. In some forms the bones about the nasal opening were swollen to form a sort of 'eagle beak'. In another type there was a thin domelike swelling over the top of the head shaped like a rooster's comb but made of bone. In others backward growth continued, to form a sort of horn projecting up and back over the neck region. It is of interest that all these peculiar structures were formed on the bones of the nasal region;

nature had, so to speak, taken the animal's nose and pulled it up over the top of its head. We have little idea what function (if any) these curious crests and horns performed. Possibly they held a reserve store of air for use in underwater feeding.

TWO ARMOURED TYPES. Since all the birdlike dinosaurs were herbivorous in habits, speedy locomotion was of service only in escaping from their carnivorous cousins. We find that several groups of ornithischians had (parallel to the developments in the other group) slumped back to a four-footed mode of life but with their ancestry clearly shown by the short front legs. These slow-moving types invariably were armed in some way against attack by the great flesh-eaters. Even in the stem archosaurs there is frequently found a double row of small bony plates down the length of the back. In *Stegosaurus* of the Jurassic these protective devices had been put to good use. They had been expanded upward to form a stout double row of bony plates covering the back and two pairs of sharp spikes near the tip of the tail. These structures obviously were useful in defence against attack from above, but the flanks appear to have had little protection.

In the Cretaceous we find a different type of armoured dinosaur in *Ankylosaurus* and its relatives. These forms have been not inaptly termed reptilian 'tanks'. The body was broad and flat and studded with a heavy series of bony nodules forming a protective layer not dissimilar to the upper shell of a giant turtle. These dinosaurs could not pull their heads and limbs into the shell as could the turtles, but these parts were also protected, for there were plates of bone to reinforce the skull and large spines projected out at the sides to fend off enemies from the limbs.

HORNED DINOSAURS. A final development in four-footed birdlike types was the appearance, in the late Cretaceous, of the horned dinosaurs such as *Triceratops*. In these forms the trunk appears to have been barren of any defensive structures; everything was concentrated on head development. From the back of the skull there extended out a broad frill of bone which covered the neck region (a favourite place for attack). Then, too, there developed on the skull stout bony horns. Two of them were usually present over the eyes, much like the horns of cattle, and a third was usually present on the nose. An interesting recent find is that of a primitive horned dinosaur, *Protoceratops*, in Mongolia. This small animal belies its name, for there were almost no traces of horns; the neck frill, however, was already well developed.

EXTINCTION OF DINOSAURS. These horned forms were very abundant in late Cretaceous times, as were most of the major groups of dinosaurs. But at the end

The skull of a horned dinosaur, *Triceratops*. The horns above the eye sockets were paired; the nose horn was a single structure. The back half of the skull is an enormous bony frill covering the neck. (After Hatcher, Marsh, and Lull)

of the Cretaceous all of them disappeared completely; the reign of the ruling reptiles was over; the Age of Reptiles was at an end.

What caused the extinction of the dinosaurs is a question to which no single or certain answer can be given. It is obvious that the carnivores would necessarily have died out with the extinction of the herbivorous types upon which they preyed. For these latter, changes in vegetation, the gradual disappearance of the plants upon which they fed, and the replacement of these plants by others which were not suitable for dinosaur food may have been important factors leading toward extinction. Many dinosaurs, as we have seen, were lowland swamp and lagoon forms; and at the end of the Cretaceous land areas were rising, with a consequent reduction in such types of country. In addition, there is distinct evidence of a chilling of the climate in North America at this general time. All these factors can, more or less directly, be traced back to one major geologic event of the times – the rise of mountain systems, particularly the Rockies. This event, by raising land levels, had considerable influence on climates and physiography and secondarily on plant and animal life. Perhaps the Rocky Mountains killed the dinosaurs!

CHAPTER 7

The Origin of Birds

THE birds are a group of interesting and often delightful creatures which are regarded as forming a separate class of vertebrates and seem to us as unlike reptiles as any sort of animal could be. But, apart from their powers of flight and features connected with it, they are structurally similar to reptiles. Indeed, it is because they are so close to the ruling reptiles from which they are descended that we may best consider them here.

THE STRUCTURE OF BIRDS. Birds have been called by an old writer 'glorified reptiles'. Feathers are, in reality, almost their only distinctive feature, for almost every other character can be matched in some archosaur type. Large quills form the expanse of the wing, taking rise from the back of the forearm and from the three fused fingers in which the wing terminates. The fleshy part of the tail is reduced to a short stub; from it there arises a spreading fan of feathers, which is an effective steering organ. The rest of the body is covered with a thick, overlapping set of smaller, softer feathers which forms a very effective insulation for the retention of the bird's bodily heat.

Unlike reptiles, birds are warm-blooded, that is, they have a high and constant body temperature (in some cases several degrees above that found in man). This requires a large supply of oxygen, good lungs, and an efficient blood circulation. We have previously remarked upon the incomplete separation of fresh and 'used' blood streams in lower land forms. The birds have evolved as efficient a circulation as our own, with a four-chambered heart and but one main vessel (or aortic arch) carrying all the pure blood to the body. But this evolution in birds has taken place independently of that in mammals, for while the main vessel in man arches over to the left of the body, the birds have put their emphasis upon a similar vessel on the right side.

The nesting habit, contrasting with the usual lack of care of reptilian eggs, seems also to have been developed in connexion with flight. The eggs must be kept warm for the maintenance of body temperature in the embryo. Further, the necessity of training for the complicated business of flight seems to have

BONE-HUNTERS IN THE FIELD. A group of paleontologists from Harvard and the Carnegie Museum of Pittsburgh examining a newly discovered fossil quarry in the Eocene deposits of eastern Utah. From this quarry were obtained numerous skulls of small deerlike mammals. In the background are seen some three hundred feet of strata (mostly barren) formed in a relatively short period at the end of the Eocene.

DISCOVERY (*below*). Looking down into an excavation in which Paul C. Miller, veteran collector of the University of Chicago, is uncovering the skeleton of a primitive reptile in the Karroo desert of South Africa.

MASS-BURIAL (*above*). In most cases only one or a few individuals are found together in fossil deposits. At times, however, there are discovered areas in which large numbers of animals died and were buried together. This figure represents a slab 6′ × 8′ in size, containing the skulls and other remains of 12 large flatheaded Triassic amphibians as found in the field in a layer which included originally perhaps 100 animals. (Specimen in Museum of Comparative Zoology, Harvard.)

1

RESURRECTING A FOSSIL. These are figures of *Dimetrodon*, a long spined reptile from the Texas redbeds. *Above*, a remarkable perfect specimen of the body shown as found in the field (a specimen at the University of Chicago). At the right, Bob Witter, of Harvard, is shown 'bandaging' such a specimen in the field with burlap and plaster for safer transportation to the laboratory. *Below*, the same specimen, mounted by George Nelson. On the next page is a scene showing characteristic animals found in these beds; *Dimetrodon* plays a prominent role.

TEXAS IN LATE PALEOZOIC TIMES. A scene based on fossils of the early part of the Permian period, found most plentifully in the redbeds of western Texas. The four-footed animals of the time were primitive reptiles and amphibians. Most of the forms illustrated are archaic relatives of the mammalian ancestors, the pelycosaurs. Some of the members of this group (as *Casea*, left) had a rather normal reptilian appearance. Others, however, had specialized in the development of a sail-like structure on the back. Five such individuals shown belong to the flesh-eating type, *Dimetrodon*, the most aggressive carnivore of its day and one which, except for its spines, was close to the ancestry of the mammals. Into this group has blundered an *Edaphosaurus*, a form which likewise bore a sail (with short crossbars on the spines) but was an inoffensive herbivorous animal.

In the right foreground are specimens of *Diplocaulus*, a water-dwelling amphibian with a grotesque flat, horned skull. (From a mural by Charles R. Knight; photograph courtesy Field Museum of Natural History, Chicago.)

3

AN ENEMY OF THE ANCIENT VERTEBRATES. In the stream deposits of the Silurian there are often found, together with remains of the oldest fishes, the skeletons of Eurypterids, ancient water-dwelling arachnids related to the scorpions and the horseshoe crabs. These were predaceous and much larger than the contemporary vertebrates. *Pterygotus*, shown here, reached a length of 6½ feet, whereas most of the fishes of those days were but a few inches in length. (From Clarke and Ruedemann.)

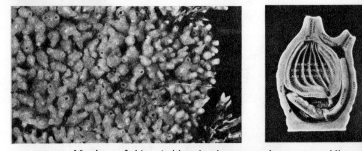

SEA SQUIRTS. Members of this primitive chordate group, known as ascidians or tunicates, are found attached to rocks or other objects in marine waters; they appear like little sacks with two round openings. *Upper left*, part of a colony of tiny tunicates (*Molgula manhattensis*) growing on a wharf pile. *Right*, a model to show the internal anatomy of such an ascidian. Water is brought in through the opening at the top, strained through an apparatus corresponding to the gills of vertebrates, and expelled through a lateral orifice. Food particles pass down into stomach and intestine. The nervous system consists only of a small ganglion from which nerve fibres radiate, and the adult lacks a notochord. (Photographs courtesy American Museum of Natural History, New York.)

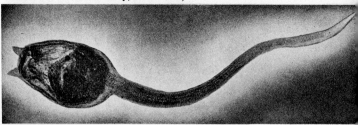

THE LARVA OF A SEA SQUIRT (*Botryllus*) (*above*). About 60 times natural size. This tiny animal contains in the large 'head' most of the structures found in the adult. The tail contains a nerve cord and notochord, visible in the photograph. After swimming about for some time, the 'head' attaches, the tail is resorbed, and the adult tunicate develops. (Photograph copyright General Biological Supply House, Chicago.)

4

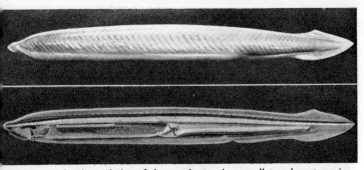

AMPHIOXUS, a chordate relative of the vertebrates, is a small translucent marine animal. At the top is an external view. Below this is a photograph of a model to show the internal anatomy. In this the animal is represented as if cut lengthwise close to the midline, the 'head' end at the left. The prominent white band running the length of the body is the notochord. Above it (in black) is the nerve cord, slightly expanded anteriorly in the position of the vertebrate brain. The striped layer above the nerve cord indicates a section taken through the muscles; the white dots are fin supports.

Below the notochord the digestive tube occupies much of the body, from the mouth at the left to the anus beneath the tail fin. Nearly half the length of the gut is occupied by the gill region (pharynx), with a highly developed lattice-work of gills. There is no distinct stomach; the hind half of the gut is a simple, straight intestine. From this a pocket branches off in front as the liver; this extends forward, mostly concealed in the model by the gill bars.

Right, a photograph of a young *Amphioxus* in which most of the same structures are readily seen. The gill lattice-work, however, is not as highly developed, and the anterior extension of the liver sac is more readily visible. (Photographs above courtesy American Museum of Natural History, New York; larva from photograph copyright by General Biological Supply House, Chicago.

BROOK LAMPREYS SPAWNING. The eggs are laid in a shallow 'nest' scooped out in the beds of a brook. The eyes and round gill openings are well shown. (Photograph courtesy New York Zoological Society.)

THE LAMPREY ATTACK (*right*). A model illustrating the mode of life of the lamprey. The round mouth sucker is applied to the skin of the prey, and the flesh is rasped off by the protrusible toothed 'tongue'. The cat-fish illustrated shows scars due to former attacks from lampreys. (Photograph courtesy American Museum of Natural History, New York.)

A CHIMAERA, or ratfish (*right, below*). A representative of a deep-sea group of fishes with cartilaginous skeletons. They are distantly related to the sharks, from which they differ in a number of respects, such as the fold of skin covering the gills (compare with the exposed gill slits of the shark below) and the peculiar jaw apparatus, suitable for mollusc-eating in the short mouth. (Photograph courtesy American Museum of Natural History, New York.)

THE SAND SHARK (*Carcharias littoralis*). Attached to its belly is the remora, or 'shark-sucker' (*Echeneis*), a higher bony fish, which thus gains a free ride and feeds on the fragments of the shark's food. A second specimen of this fish is seen at the bottom, showing the flattened head topped by a sucking device. (Photograph courtesy New York Zoological Society.)

VARIOUS SHARKS. *Above*, the whale shark (*Rhinodon*), largest of all fishes living to-day, with a length of about 50 feet in the largest known specimens. This form is rare but widespread in the warmer waters of the world. Despite its size, however, this shark is a harmless form, with very small teeth, and makes its living on minute forms of sea life. Some fossil sharks appear to have been larger, although only incompletely known. *Left*, the restored jaws of a Tertiary shark (*Carcharodon*), with a man seated therein to give an idea of the gape. This form was related to the living sand shark shown on the last page, and with its powerful dentition must have been a terror in Tertiary seas. *Below*, the hammer-head shark (*Sphyrna*), from a painting by Charles R. Knight. In this peculiar creature the eyes are placed in prominent lateral projections from the head. (Photographs courtesy American Museum of Natural History, New York.)

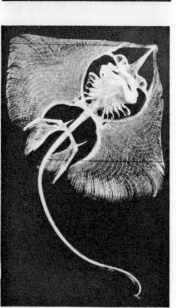

SKATES AND RAYS. A rather successful side branch of the shark group are the skates and rays, depressed-bodied forms with the teeth flattened into crushing plates for feeding on molluscs and other invertebrates. These bottom-dwellers have lost the typical body form of their shark relatives. The tail has become a whip-like structure, while the pectoral fins (corresponding to the arms of land vertebrates) are greatly enlarged, as may be seen from the figure of the skeleton, and even meet in front of the nose. Swimming is accomplished by undulations of these fins. The form figured is the prickly skate (*Raja scabrata*), common on the northern part of the Atlantic coast. *Top left* shows the dorsal surface. The large opening back of the eyes is the spiracle, a specialized first gill slit through which water is taken in. On the white under surface can be seen the nostrils, mouth, and gill slits. The skate on the left is a female; that shown from the underside is a male, with long claspers on the pelvic fins for internal fertilization of the eggs. (Photographs courtesy American Museum of Natural History, New York.)

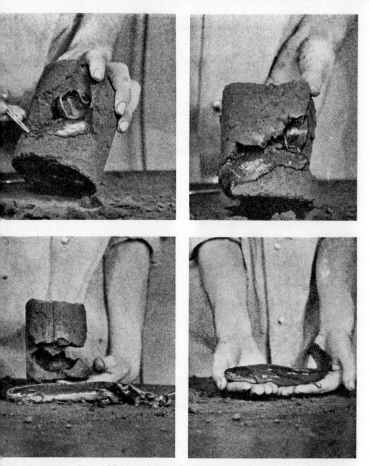

CANNED LUNGFISH. The African and South American lungfish have the ability to burrow into the bottom and pass the season of drought in a mud 'cocoon'. It has been found that the African form (*Protopterus*), illustrated here, can be persuaded to form its cocoon in a tin can and thus be readily transported. When desired, the can may be opened and the fish removed; on placing it in the water it soon resumes its normal activities. This potentiality of passing a hot or dry season in a condition of reduced body activity is termed aestivation and corresponds to the hibernation of many animals in cold climates. Above are shown stages in the opening-up of a canned lungfish. On the next page is shown a specimen in an aquarium shortly after removal. (Photographs copyright General Biological Supply House, Chicago.)

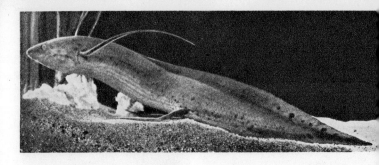

FISH RELATIVES OF LAND ANIMALS. *Above* the African lungfish (*Protopterus*). Although the living lungfish are quite specialized in a number of regards, they retain many features to be expected in ancestors of land types. Closer, however, to this ancestry are the lobe-finned fishes (Order CROSSOPTERYGII), two examples of which are illustrated. The group is nearly extinct. *Left*, a restoration of *Eusthenopteron*, a fossil Devonian form frequently found in American deposits. Its fins appear to have been stout enough to support it, as shown here, on a stream bank. *Below, Latimeria*, the only surviving lobefin, known from a single specimen, a five-foot blue-coloured fish recently caught off the South African coast. This deep-sea relict type is obviously a highly specialized side line of the lobefin stock. (*Protopterus*, courtesy New York Zoological Society; *Eusthenopteron*, from a painting by F. L. Jaques under the direction of W. K. Gregory; courtesy American Museum of Natural History, New York; *Latimeria*, from a photograph by its describer, J. L. B. Smith.)

FOUR PRIMITIVE RAY-FINNED FISHES. Most living rayfins are teleosts – the highest sub-division of the series. Of the few survivors of more primitive actinopterygians, a majority, those illustrated on this page, are found in the United States. *Top*, the paddlefish, or 'spoonbill cat' (*Polyodon*), of the Mississippi, a form which may reach 200 pounds in weight. It is degenerate in many ways and has become a bottom-dwelling mud-grubber with a long, spoon-shaped snout but still retains a sharklike tail. Next *below*, the sturgeon (*Acipenser*) also rather degenerate; note the peculiar 'feelers' in advance of the mouth. Little cherished except for caviar, the sturgeons are found in various regions of the northern continents, including the Mississippi Valley and Great Lakes. Third, the bowfin, or 'fresh-water dogfish' (*Amia*), a form not far below the teleost level. It is a common lake fish of the Middle West and South. (Continued on next page)

11

THE GAR PIKE (*Lepidosteus*) is a Mississippi Valley inhabitant, notable as one of the few living fishes which have retained the thick ganoid scales of early fishes. The form shown is the giant alligator gar of the southern states. (*Polyodon, Lepidosteus,* photographs courtesy American Museum of Natural History; *Acipenser, Amia,* courtesy New York Zoological Society.)

THE MOST PRIMITIVE RAY-FINNED FISH. A restoration of *Cheirolepis* of the Middle Devonian, the oldest and most primitive member of the actinopterygians. (From a painting by F. L. Jaques, under the direction of W. K. Gregory.)

AN AUSTRALIAN SEA HORSE (*Phyllopteryx*), *left.* This grotesque little fish differs from the ordinary sea horse in peculiar outgrowths suggesting seaweed. (Photograph courtesy American Museum of Natural History.)

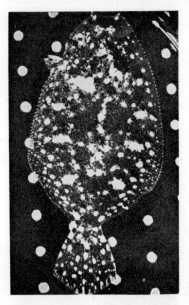

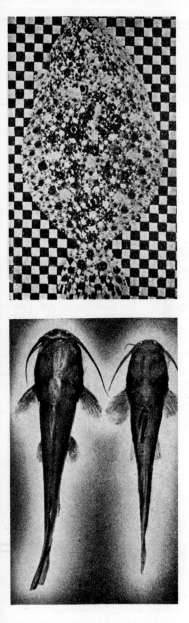

COLOUR CHANGE IN FISHES. *Left*, two catfish kept for a day in dishes with light and dark backgrounds, respectively, showing response in colour change of the animal. *Above*, two photographs of the same specimen of flounder placed on different backgrounds; in this form there is a tendency for change not merely in colour but in pattern as well. Such changes are initiated by vision, for if the animal is blinded, the skin becomes permanently dark, and there is no response to the environment. The colour changes are effected chemically by neurohumours, substances given off either by near-by skin nerves or by the pituitary. (Catfish, courtesy G. H. Parker; flounders after S. O. Mast.)

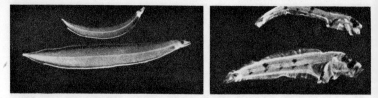

LARVAL TELEOSTS. The young of the bony fishes are often quite different from the adult. *Left*, larval eels, termed *Leptocephalus*. These are thin, translucent, and leaf shaped. The larva of the European eel attains a length of 3 inches before a marked change takes place, transforming the 'leaf' into a smaller, cylindrical baby eel. *Right*, tiny flounders. In contrast to the pancake-shaped adult, the young have a slender body. The side seen is the future upper side; note that both eyes (seen as black dots) are already on this surface, the left eye having migrated around the upper edge of the head. (Photographs courtesy H. C. Bigelow.)

UNUSUAL TELEOSTS. Many of the more normal modern bony fishes may be observed on the dinner table. Below and over page are figured some of the more abnormal types:

DEEP-SEA FISHES. In the lightless depths of the ocean are numbers of teleosts which have become adapted to the unusual conditions there. In this scene (from a museum exhibit) a carnivore with an enormous mouth (*Chauliodus*) is seen pursuing a flock of 'big-heads' (*Melamphids*). (Photograph courtesy American Museum of Natural History, New York.)

THE FOUR-EYED FISH (*Anableps*). A small fish of the American tropics which swims at the surface. Each eye is divided into two parts externally, the upper part adapted for vision in air, the lower for water vision.

THE SEA ROBINS (*Prionotus*) are common fishes of the Atlantic coast, usually found on the bottom in shallow waters; when disturbed they may bury themselves to the eyes in sand. The front rays of the pectoral fins are separately movable as rather spiderish-looking feelers which can be used as digging organs. (Photographs courtesy New York Zoological Society.)

THE MUDSKIPPER (*Periophthalmus*), which lives along the coasts of the Old World tropics. Unlike ordinary teleosts, the fish has muscular fins by means of which it is able to leave the water and crawl over the mud-flats and the roots and lower branches of mangroves near the water.

THE ELECTRIC EEL. This fish (*Gymnotus*) of the Orinoco and Amazon regions is eel-like in shape but actually a relative of the carp and catfish. Its peculiarity (shared with several other fishes) is that parts of its muscular system are so modified as to have become a powerful electric battery. The voltage averages about 550 volts; it can be drawn on for enough power to light more than a dozen ordinary lamp bulbs enough for a flat.

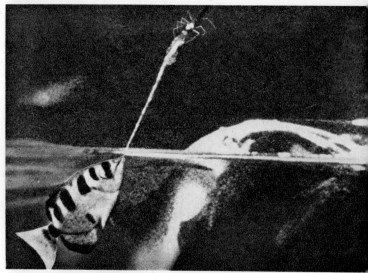

THE ARCHER FISH (*Toxotes*) of the East Indies derives its name from the fact that it can accurately shoot drops of water to capture insects or spiders near the surface. (All photographs courtesy New York Zoological Society.)

16

PRIMITIVE FOUR-FOOTED ANIMALS. Restoration of early amphibians (labyrinthodonts, genus *Diplovertebron*) of Carboniferous days. These ancient forms spent much of their lives in the water but nevertheless possessed the ability to walk on land. (Painting by F. L. Jaques under the direction of W. K. Gregory; photograph courtesy American Museum of Natural History.)

WALKING SALAMANDER – a newt of the genus *Pseudotriton* photographed from above. Much of the progression of the body is accomplished, as in the ancestral fish, by throwing the body into sinuous curves. (Photograph by Sherman C. Bishop.)

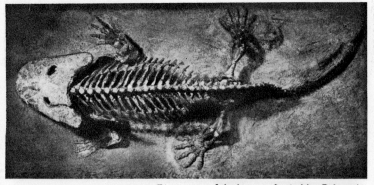

SKELETON OF A FOSSIL AMPHIBIAN, *Eryops*, one of the largest of primitive Paleozoic amphibians, seen from above. This figure illustrates well the sprawled pose of the limbs in early land types and still retained in the salamander shown above. (Photograph courtesy American Museum of Natural History.)

17

THE AXOLOTL, an amphibian Peter Pan. *Left*, the common American orange and black tiger salamander (*Amblystoma tigrinum*). In the figure below (*left*) immersed in the water is the axolotl; a salamander from Mexico and the Rockies, supposedly of quite a different sort – a permanent water dweller breathing by means of gills. It is now known that the axolotl is merely a variety of tiger salamander which tends to remain throughout life in a larval condition. However, various stimuli (including the feeding of thyroid) may cause them to change into the true adult form. (*A. tigrinum*, copyright General Biological Supply House, Chicago; axolotl, courtesy New York Zoological Society.)

THE MUD PUPPY (*Necturus*) (*above*) a large salamander, well over a foot in length when adult, found in many parts of the Mississippi Valley. Like the axolotl the mud puppy is a permanent larva, for it never leaves the water and retains gills. In this case, however, no stimulus can make the animal change into the supposed adult condition; it has, so to speak, forgotten how to grow up. (Photograph courtesy New York Zoological Society.)

A CAVE SALAMANDER. In several instances salamanders have become adapted to underground life. The specimen shown directly *above* is a cave salamander (*Lyphlotriton*), photographed in an Ozark cave. It is blind and nearly colourless. (Photograph by G. K. Noble, courtesy American Museum of Natural History, New York.)

THE 'CONGO EEL', which is not an eel or a native of the Congo, but a salamander (*Amphiuma*) inhabiting swamps and sluggish streams of the southern states. It is, however, no wonder that it is termed an eel, for it is a degenerate water dweller in which the limbs are reduced to tiny vestiges. (Photograph courtesy American Museum of Natural History, New York.)

METAMORPHOSIS of a common frog (*Rana clamitans*) from a typical tadpole at the lower left to a mature frog at the upper right. Development of hind legs, appearance of front legs, and resorption of tail occur in order. (Photograph copyright General Biological Supply House, Chicago.)

THE SPRING PEEPER (tree toad, genus *Hyla*) in action (*right*). Sound production is aided by the enormous inflated voca'l sac. (Photograph by Dr Frank Overton, courtesy American Museum Natural History, New York.)

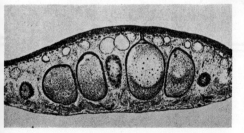

FROG SKIN (*left*), a section, highly magnified. Above, the thin outer skin (epidermis); below, the thicker dermis. In the latter are numerous globular glands. The smaller are mucous glands; the larger secrete a mildly poisonous material. (Photomicrograph copyright General Biological Supply House, Chicago.)

19

A BURROWING, LIMBLESS AMPHIBIAN belonging to the order APODA and only distantly related to the salamanders and frogs. These burrowers are small and wormlike, with rudimentary eyes but with sensory tentacles between eye and nostril. The Apoda are tropical types; the form illustrated (*Ichthyopis*) is from the East Indies. In this form the eggs are kept in a moist burrow and protected by the female. (From the Sarasins.)

SMALL BUT POISONOUS. A tiny South American toad (*Dendrobates*) shown at the right, natural size, perched on a copper cent. The liquid from its skin glands is used by South American natives to poison arrow tips. (Photograph courtesy New York Zoological Society.)

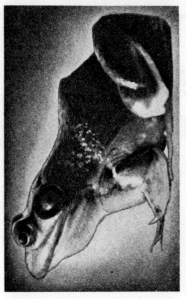

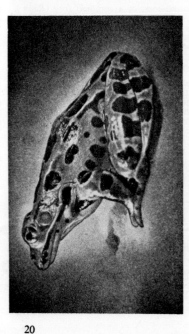

TWO COMMON FROGS. *Left*, the leopard or grass frog; *right*, the bullfrog. Both are familiar forms in the field, and both are frequent in biological laboratories. (Photographs copyright General Biological Supply House, Chicago.)

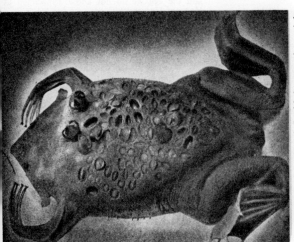

THE SURINAM TOAD (*Pipa*). In this large and ungainly South American toad the eggs are not laid in the water but become inclosed in the skin of the mother's back, each in a little pocket covered by a flap. When development is completed, small but maturely formed little toads emerge – the water stage is eliminated. (From a model, courtesy American Museum of Natural History, New York.)

THE HAIRY FROG (*Astylosternus*) of Africa. In the male, at breeding season, hair-like projections grow out of the sides of the trunk and legs. These, however, are not hairs but accessory breathing organs – outgrowths of the skin containing blood vessels. (Photograph copyright General Biological Supply House, Chicago.)

THE OLDEST EGG. The object left, as proved by microscopic study, is a fossil egg and by far the world's oldest, since it comes from Texas deposits of late Paleozoic age, perhaps 225,000,000 years or so old. A number of primitive reptiles were then present; which one laid the egg we do not know. (Specimen at Harvard University.)

AN ARCHAIC REPTILE (*left*). *Seymouria*, named from the Texas town near which its remains were discovered, is a fossil form so primitive in nature that it retains numerous amphibian features. The animal, tail and all, was less than a yard in length. (Painting by F. L. Jaques, under the direction of W. K. Gregory; photograph courtesy American Museum of Natural History, New York.)

AN AMERICAN CROCODILE (*right*). The familiar American crocodilian is the broad-snouted alligator of the southern United States. However the crocodiles, while mainly Old World forms, are also represented in tropical America, and one species is present in Florida. While the Old World crocodiles are dreaded, the American species are mainly fish-eaters and do not appear to be particularly dangerous to man. (Photograph courtesy New York Zoological Society.)

A CROCODILE PREDECESSOR (*Right*). The extinct phytosaurs of the Triassic period were an offshoot of the early ruling reptiles that had habits similiar to the modern crocodilians; although related, they were not ancestral to the crocodiles. Their adaptations for an amphibious flesh-eating mode of life were similar to those of crocodiles, except that the nostrils were situated at the top of the head in front of the eyes. (From a drawing by S. W. Williston.)

22

A JURASSIC SCENE on a coral island in Germany. Jurassic deposits at several points in Europe, particularly southern Germany, consist of a fine-grained limestone used for lithography. This material appears to have been deposited in the quiet shallow waters of lagoons in coral islands in the warm seas that then covered much of Europe. The sediments are so fine that remains of many small and delicate creatures are preserved. Several of the more interesting vertebrates are shown here amid a foliage of cycads and other Mesozoic plants of tropical appearance. In the air are small flying reptiles of the genus *Rhamphorhynchus*, with a long, keeled tail. Fluttering about or perched on a cycad are the most primitive birds, of the *Archaeopteryx* type, known only from these deposits. The two small animals at the left are dinosaurs of the genus *Compsognathus*, no larger than a rooster but nevertheless related to the large flesh-eating dinosaurs. (From a mural by Charles R. Knight; photograph courtesy Field Museum of Natural History, Chicago.)

DINOSAUR FOOTPRINTS. In the Connecticut Valley are great deposits of sandstone of Triassic age, once quarried for sidewalk slabs, etc. In various places these have revealed numerous footprints of dinosaurs. A major collection is that at Amherst College (including the specimen figured). The footprints shown are three-toed. They are, of course, comparable to those of birds and were long supposed to have been made by gigantic birds.

23

THE OSTRICH DINOSAUR (*Struthiomimus*). This was a Cretaceous bipedal flesh-eater related to the giant carnivores but of relatively small size. The bulk was about that of an ostrich. Ostrich-like, too, were the proportions of hind legs and neck and the small head with a toothless bill. However, a characteristic dinosaur tail was present, and the three-fingered 'hand' was well developed. This creature's habits are not surely known, but it may well have been an egg-stealer. (Restoration by Erwin Christman; photograph courtesy American Museum of Natural History, New York.)

THE SKULL OF *Tyrannosaurus*. The skull of this great flesh-eater of the Cretaceous measured some 4 feet in length and was armed with a powerful battery of sharp, compressed and recurved teeth. (Photograph courtesy American Musuem of Natural History, New York.)

UPPER CRETACEOUS DINOSAURS. Two of the most spectacular types of dinosaurs are shown here in a scene that may well have occurred in Western North America at the very end of the Age of Reptiles; the forms illustrated were contemporaries in Wyoming deposits. *Tyrannosaurus* (*right*) was the giant among the large carnivorous dinosaurs, with a length of about 47 feet and a height in standing pose of about 19 feet. There was a large head with sharp and powerful teeth and massive hind legs; the 'arms,' however, were absurdly small. A pair of these creatures are shown about to attack the horned dinosaur *Triceratops*, a harmless herbivorous type. This reptile was defended by sharp horns and a bony frill over the vulnerable neck region. The rest of the body, however, was covered merely with a leather hide, and hence we may assume that a successful defence necessitated keeping the head face to face with the enemy. (From a mural by Charles R. Knight; photograph courtesy Field Museum of Natural History, Chicago.)

25

UPPER CRETACEOUS DINOSAURS (*continued*). Another scene at the close of the Age of Reptiles, but slightly earlier and from another locality – western Canada just east of the rising Rocky Mountains. This country had been previously covered by the sea and was (rather in contrast with present conditions) a lowland, well-watered, with numerous swamps and lagoons. Most of the dinosaurs shown are harmless herbivores belonging to the birdlike group (*Ornithischia*). In the left foreground is a heavily armoured quadrupedal dinosaur (*Palaeoscincus*) covered with bony plates and with spines projecting out over the limbs; the tail, too, was a powerful, bony clublike weapon. At the right are crestless members of the bipedal duckbill dinosaur group (hadrosaurs or trachodonts). These herbivores appear to have been more or less amphibious, with webbed feet. Many of the duckbills developed peculiar crests on top of the skull. Two crested types are seen at the left – *Corythsaurus* in the foreground, a group of individuals of *Parasaurolophus* behind. In the centre background are ostrich-like dinosaurs (*Ornithomimus*). (From a mural by Charles R. Knight; photograph courtesy Field Museum of Natural History, Chicago.)

A GIANT AMPHIBIOUS DINOSAUR (*Brontosaurus*) from the Upper Jurassic of the West. Great areas in the regions now occupied by the Rocky Mountains and the adjacent high plains in Utah, Colorado, and Wyoming were, in the late Jurassic, lowlands with meandering streams and bayous and a rich vegetation; the region may have been rather comparable in nature to the present Mississippi Delta country. In these lagoons lived great amphibious (or sauropod) dinosaurs, such as the form shown here, and the closely related *Diplodocus*, *Brachiosaurus*, etc. Although for pictorial purposes one of these giants is shown ashore, it is probable that they spent nearly their entire existence in the lagoons, where the buoyancy of the water would render the burden of their great weight less onerous.

Primitive crocodiles were present in the same region; several of them are shown in the foreground. (From a mural by Charles R. Knight; photograph courtesy Field Museum of Natural History, Chicago.)

Stegosaurus. One of the most familiar members of the dinosaur group is this late Jurassic form, a four-footed herbivore armed with a double row of plates and spines down the back. (From a mural by Charles R. Knight; photograph courtesy Field Museum of Natural History, Chicago.)

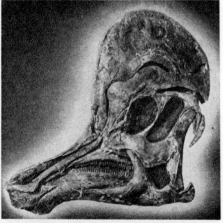

A CRESTED DINOSAUR. In many of the Cretaceous duckbilled dinosaurs peculiar out-growths occurred on the top of the skull, formed by the bones normally surrounding the nostrils and containing air tubes which may have been of use in the partially aquatic life of these dinosaurs. *Corythosaurus*, whose skull is figured here, is shown in a landscape two plates toward the front. (Photograph courtesy American Museum of Natural History, New York.)

A PRIMITIVE HORNED DINOSAUR (*Protoceratops*) from the Cretaceous of Mongolia. This small reptile (the largest specimen only about 6 feet long) was an ancestor of the great horned dinosaurs, but one in which the horns were still undeveloped. (From a mural by Charles R. Knight; photograph courtesy Field Museum of Natural History, Chicago.)

DINOSAUR EGGS. Closely associated with the remains of the small horned dinosaur shown above were numerous eggs found in 'nests' of a dozen or so. (Photograph courtesy American Museum of Natural History, New York.)

A SMALL FLYING REPTILE (*Pterodactylus*) from the Jurassic lithographic stone of Germany. Except that this is a short-tailed form the skeletal elements can be readily compared with those shown in text figure in the sub-section on 'Flying Reptiles', in Chapter 6.

THE OLDEST BIRDS. Of Jurassic birds the only known remains are the two skeletons shown on this page and an isolated feather. All were found in the lithographic limestone of southern Germany half to three-quarters of a century ago, and not another scrap has been discovered since. *Left*, the specimen in the Berlin museum (named *Archæornis*); a nearly complete skeleton, showing all four limbs and tail and with the head twisted back to the left; the feathers are well displayed. *Bottom right*, the other skeleton, in the British Museum; this individual (known as *Archaeopteryx*) is less complete. *Bottom left*, a restoration of a pair of these birds; the colour scheme is, of course, imaginary. Another restoration was shown in an earlier plate. The bird in life was about the size of a crow. (Restoration from Heilmann, *Fuglenes Afstamning*.)

THE KING PENGUIN. The Southern Hemisphere contains a great variety of these flightless, strong-winged swimmers. Mainly Antarctic, they are, however, found as far north as the Cape of Good Hope, and there is even a colony on the Galapagos. The king penguin is a large form inhabiting the Falklands, Kerguelen, and other southern islands. (Photograph courtesy New York Zoological Society.)

THE WORLD'S BOLDEST NAVIGATORS – THE PLOVERS. The tiny golden plovers migrate annually from the Arctic to the Southern Hemisphere. The voyages of the plover which nests in Canada are discussed in the text. The Alaskan form (*right*) makes non-stop flights to the Hawaiian Islands and return in the course of its migration to and from the South Seas. (Photograph courtesy New York Zoological Society.)

A CRETACEOUS DIVING BIRD. Relatively few birds are known from the Cretaceous, but such evidence as we have shows that birds were already diversified and specialized at that time, although still retaining teeth. *Left*, a restoration of *Hesperornis*, a flightless diver known from the chalk rocks of Kansas. It had somewhat the proportions of a modern loon and probably had similar habits. (From Heilmann, *The Origin of Birds*, copyright D. Appleton-Century Co., used by permission.)

31

HUMMING BIRDS ON THE WING. These tiny birds have such rapid wing movements – on the general order of 50 beats or more per second – that in flight they appear but a blur to the eye to an ordinary fast camera. Modern physics, however, has produced the stroboscopic camera, which can photograph objects by extremely bright but extremely short flashes of light. By this means these birds were photographed (by Harold E. Edgerton, of Massachusetts Institute of Technology) as if 'frozen' in midair. (The 'bait', incidentally, consisted of a mixture of honey, condensed milk, and baby food.)

variety of flightless birds which were able to exist there because of the absence of terrestrial enemies. All are now extinct except the kiwi (genus *Apteryx*), shown (*left*). These birds are of moderate height, rather larger than domestic fowls. They are nocturnal; the long bill is used in probing for worms, which form the principal portion of their diet. The eggs, as may be seen, are relatively enormous. Although of smaller size, the kiwi is believed to be related to the ostrich and other 'ratites'. (Photograph courtesy American Museum of Natural History, New York.)

THE HEATH HEN (*below right*) was closely related to the prairie hen of the western plains and more distantly related to the grouse and other game birds. It was once found in many areas of the eastern United States, but a century ago survived only on Martha's Vineyard. Here a flock remained with slowly dwindling numbers until 1932, when the last survivor, illustrated here, died. (Photograph courtesy Dr A. O. Gross, Bowdoin College.)

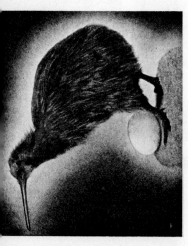

BIRDS RECENTLY EXTINCT. Within the time of recorded history there have been numerous cases of birds which have become extinct. The great auk and the passenger pigeon are examples; others, shown here, are the dodo (*right*) and the heath hen (*far right*). The dodo was a flightless bird related to the pigeons and in size rather larger than a turkey. It was abundant on Mauritius, in the western Indian Ocean, when that island was first discovered. Man and domestic animals introduced by him, however, caused its extermination before the close of the seventeenth century. Unfortunately, skeletons alone have been preserved; but from excellent paintings have been made replicas such as that illustrated. (Photograph courtesy American Museum of Natural History, New York.)

THE FOUR LIVING GREAT RATITES. The birds illustrated on this page are all large flightless types which show many similarities in build and, with the kiwi, are usually regarded as forming a group termed ratites. *Upper left*, the familiar ostrich, a desert type of Africa, once widespread over Asia as well. A notable peculiarity is the reduction of the toes to two rather than the three toes common in most birds. *Upper right*, the cassowary of Australia and New Guinea, with a characteristic casque of bony tissue atop the head. *Lower left*, the emu, also an Australian resident; note the very different coloration of the young. *Lower right*, the rhea of the South American pampas. (Photographs courtesy New York Zoological Society.)

EXTINCT GIANT BIRDS. In past times there existed many flightless birds, some of them much larger than birds now living. *Above*, some of the moas of New Zealand which resembled the living ratites in general build but in some instances reached a height of 10½ feet. Although now extinct, they existed there so recently that 'fresh' bones and even feathers have been preserved. *Lower left*, *Phororhacos*, a giant type from the Miocene of Patagonia, which stood about 4 feet in height and (unlike the ratites) had a large head and powerful beak. *Lower right*, *Diatryma* from the early Eocene of Wyoming. This bird was about 7 feet tall; the contemporary horses were but the size of a fox terrier. (Moas from a mural by Charles R. Knight; photograph courtesy Field Museum of Natural History, Chicago. *Phororhacos* and *Diatryma*, courtesy American Museum of Natural History, New York.)

A COMMON AMERICAN LIZARD, the 'mountain boomer', or collared lizard (*Crotaphytus*), abundant in the semiarid regions of the Southwest. This is a form of fairly good size, averaging a foot or so in length, and related to the large iguana lizards of the American tropics. (Photograph copyright General Biological Supply House, Chicago.)

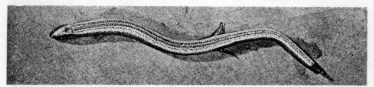

A SHORT-LEGGED LIZARD (*Neoseps*). In various lizard groups there has been a tendency for reduction of the limbs. The little Florida reptile shown here belongs to a family known as the skinks, most of which, however, have normal limbs. *Above*, is shown a lizard in which with further reduction the limbs have been entirely lost. (Photograph courtesy American Museum of Natural History, New York.)

THE GIANT LIZARD OF KOMODO. The monitor lizards of the Old World tropics (genus *Varanus*) are generally forms of large size; largest of all is the species found on the little island of Komodo in Indonesia. Early reports of these 'dragons' were that they were 30 feet or so in length. However, like most monsters, they shrank upon investigation. The largest is but 10 feet in length. Even so, they are very large reptiles. A pig is acceptable bait. (Photograph courtesy American Museum of Natural History, New York.)

THE HORNED 'TOAD'. This little animal, so abundant in the drier regions of southwest U.S.A., is not a toad but a lizard (*Phrynosoma*), although one with a peculiarly broad and flattened body. A considerable degree of protection is afforded it by its horny spines. Were it of larger size its odd appearance would be considered as grotesque as that, for example, of the horned dinosaurs. (Photograph by Raymond L. Ditmars, courtesy New York Zoological Society.)

THE FLYING DRAGON. This lizard (*Draco volans*), a native of the East Indies, is able to expand membranes on either side of the body which form a parachute device. The membranes are supported by specialized movable ribs. (Photograph by Raymond L. Ditmars, courtesy New York Zoological Society.)

THE CHAMELEON. The true chameleons are grotesque inhabitants of the Old World tropics, principally Africa. They are specialized in numerous features such as the prehensile tail, the cleft feet, well adapted for grasping limbs, and the long tongue, readily protusible for seizing insect prey. (Photograph courtesy New York Zoological Society.)

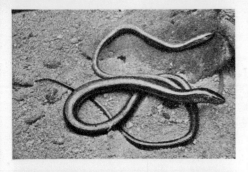

LIMBLESS LIZARDS. In a number of different families of lizards the limbs have been lost and a snakelike appearance results. These forms, however, can be readily distinguished from the true snakes by the structure of the skull and various other characters. *Left*, a species of the 'glass-snake' (*Ophisaurus*), a limbless lizard found in both North America and Eurasia. Still more specialized is the 'blind worm' (*Anguis*) of Europe (*centre*). This tiny creature is, as the comparison in the photograph indicates, no larger than an earthworm, and rather resembles that creature. It is, however, not 'blind', for the eyes, though small, are well developed. (*Ophisaurus* courtesy New York Zoological Society; *Anguis* courtesy American Museum of Natural History, New York.)

THE GILA MONSTER (*Heloderma*), the only poisonous lizard. (Photograph courtesy American Museum of Natural History, New York.)

38

THE KING COBRA of southeastern Asia, giant of poisonous snakes, with a maximum length of 18 feet. (Photograph courtesy New York Zoological Society.)

A GIANT SNAKE. The anaconda of South America is a boa somewhat amphibious in habits. It has been recorded to reach a length of 46 feet; this is doubtful, however, and 30 feet may be a maximum. (Photograph courtesy New York Zoological Society.)

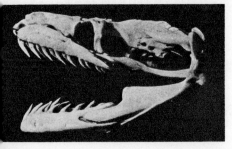

THE SNAKE SKULL. This is a nonpoisonous form, the royal python. Teeth are numerous and directed backward, every movement forcing the prey down the throat. The whole jaw apparatus is loosely constructed, rendering easy distension of the throat. (Photograph courtesy American Museum of Natural History, New York.)

39

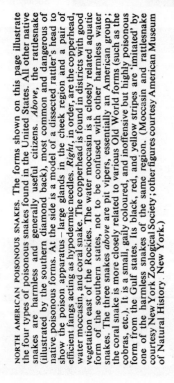

NORTH AMERICAN POISONOUS SNAKES. The forms shown on this page illustrate the four types of poisonous snakes found in the United States. All other native snakes are harmless and generally useful citizens. *Above*, the rattlesnake (illustrated by the southern diamond back), most common and dangerous of native poisonous forms. At the side is a model of a dissected rattler's head to show the poison apparatus – large glands in the cheek region and a pair of efficient fangs acting as hypodermic needles. *Right*, in order, are the copperhead, water moccasin, and coral snake. The copperhead is found in districts with good vegetation east of the Rockies. The water moccasin is a closely related aquatic form of the southern states, not to be confused with other harmless water snakes. The three snakes *above* are pit vipers, essentially an American group; the coral snake is more closely related to various Old World forms (such as the cobras, etc.). It is a small, gaily coloured, and inoffensive but highly poisonous form from the Gulf states. Its black, red, and yellow stripes are 'imitated' by one of the harmless snakes of the same region. (Moccasin and rattlesnake courtesy New York Zoological Society; other figures courtesy American Museum of Natural History. New York.)

40

KANSAS IN THE CRETACEOUS. Near the end of the Age of Reptiles much of America was covered by shallow seas filled with an abundant vertebrate life. Chalk rocks of this age bearing numerous fossils are well represented in western Kansas. Some of the characteristic forms are shown here. *Centre*, a mosasaur (*Clidastes*), a great marine lizard distantly related to the terrestrial monitor lizards of the Old World. *Right*, a giant marine turtle (*Archelon*), an early representative of a group that has survived to grace the soup tureen to-day. Soaring above the waters are a number of giant flying reptiles of the genus *Pteranodon* – tailless forms characterized by a long crest at the back of the head. Other common members of the fauna but not illustrated are plesiosaurs, toothed birds, and a great variety of fishes. (From a mural by Charles R. Knight; photograph courtesy Field Museum of Natural History, Chicago.)

41

THE TUATERA of New Zealand (*Sphenodon*), an archaic reptile. This small and sluggish reptile resembles the lizards in many ways, but the two-arched construction of its skull shows that it is the only surviving member of a separate order of reptiles (Rhynchocephalia) which has existed since the Triassic period. Its survival appears to be due to geographic isolation in New Zealand. *Left*, the skeleton of an almost identical fossil form from the Jurassic (*Homoeosaurus*). (*Sphenodon* courtesy American Musuem of Natural History, New York; *Homoeosaurus* from a specimen in Harvard University.)

MARINE TURTLES. The green (soup) and hawksbill (tortoise-shell) species. (Photographs courtesy New York Zoological Society.)

TCH-HIKERS. A pair of remoras stealing a
de with a marine turtle. (Photograph
urtesy New York Zoological Society.)

THE LEATHERY TURTLE (*Dermochelys*), A
giant marine form, but one not at all
closely related to the normal marine
turtles shown on the opposite page. Of
the bony shell only small nubbins of
bone remain, and the horny shield is
likewise absent and replaced by a tough
leathery hide. This is the largest living
turtle, with a record weight of nearly a
ton and a length of 8 feet. (Photograph
courtesy American Museum of Natural
History, New York.)

THE SNAPPING TURTLE (*Chelydra*), *left*.
The snappers are vicious water dwellers
in North American streams, notable for
large heads and large tails – unusual in
turtles. (Photograph courtesy New York
Zoological Society.)

HE AUSTRALIAN SNAKE-NECKED TURTLE
Chelodina), *right*. This long-necked
orm is a representative of a primitive
urtle group, the 'side-necked' turtles
pleurodires), found only in southern
ontinents. Instead of pulling the neck
traight into the shell, it is tucked in side-
vays along the shoulder. (Photograph
ourtesy American Museum of Natural
History, New York.)

A GIANT TORTOISE (*left*). The tortoises of
the genus *Testudo*, in contrast to most
turtles, are purely land dwellers, characterized by a high, domelike carapace.
Some species found on oceanic islands
grow to large size. Several such species
are present in the Galápagos and others
on islands in the Indian Ocean. The
form figured is from the Aldabra Islands. Record weights are over 500
pounds and lengths run to 6 feet. How
these land dwellers reached such oceanic
islands is a mystery. (Photograph courtesy New York Zoological Society.)

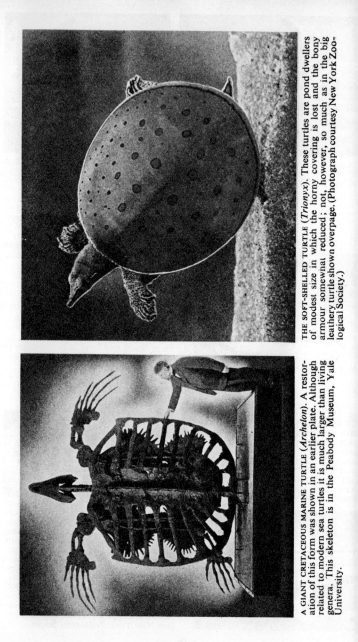

A GIANT CRETACEOUS MARINE TURTLE (*Archelon*). A restoration of this form was shown in an earlier plate. Although related to modern sea turtles it is much larger than living genera. This skeleton is in the Peabody Museum, Yale University.

THE SOFT-SHELLED TURTLE (*Trionyx*). These turtles are pond dwellers of modest size in which the horny covering is lost and the bony armour somewhat reduced; not, however, so much as in the big leathery turtle shown overpage. (Photograph courtesy New York Zoological Society.)

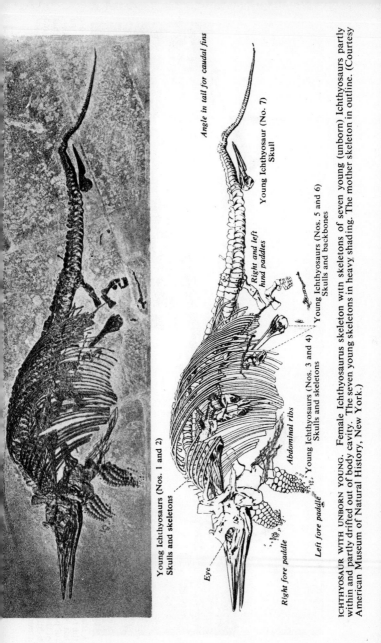

Young Ichthyosaurs (Nos. 1 and 2)
Skulls and skeletons

Angle in tail for caudal fins

Young Ichthyosaur (No. 7)
Skull

Right and left
hind paddles

Young Ichthyosaurs (Nos. 5 and 6)
Skulls and backbones

Abdominal ribs

Young Ichthyosaurs (Nos. 3 and 4)
Skulls and skeletons

Eye

Left fore paddle

Right fore paddle

ICHTHYOSAUR WITH UNBORN YOUNG. Female Ichthyosaurus skeleton witn skeletons of seven young (unborn) Ichthyosaurs partly within and partly drifted out of body cavity. The seven young skeletons in heavy shading. The mother skeleton in outline. (Courtesy American Museum of Natural History, New York.)

45

A JURASSIC SEA. European deposits of this age have revealed an abundant fauna of marine animals of all types. Particularly interesting are the two types of reptiles illustrated here which have left the land and returned to the water to become highly specialized aquatic types. On the left is a group of plesiosaurs. These forms had a broad flat body and swam by strokes of their limbs, which had been transformed into powerful paddles. Frequently, as in the form illustrated, the neck had become greatly elongated. A second and more highly specialized type is that of the ichthyosaurs, two of which are shown at the right. These were good reptiles but had re-assumed a typical fish shape and had re-acquired fishlike fins. They seem to have been similar in form and habits to modern porpoises, although of course they are not related to them. (From a mural by Charles R. Knight; photograph courtesy Field Museum of Natural History, Chicago.)

AN ANCIENT MAMMAL JAW. Mammals from the Age of Reptiles are known from very fragmentary materials. A jaw, such as is shown here, is about as good as they come. These older mammals were almost universally of tiny size, in strong contrast with the contemporary giant reptiles. The specimen shown was rather smaller than the illustration. (After Simpson.)

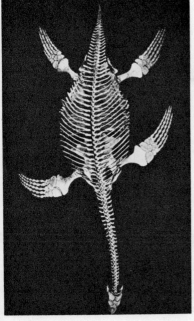

A PLESIOSAUR SKELETON, viewed from above. This specimen shows well the small head, slender neck, broad flat body, and powerful swimming limbs of typical plesiosaurs. (Photograph courtesy American Museum of Natural History, New York.)

MAMMAL-LIKE REPTILES (right). A scene in the Karroo region of South Africa in early Triassic times. A group of cynodonts – advanced mammal-like forms – about to attack a dicynodont or 'two-tusker', an aberrant herbivorous member of the same group. (From a mural by Charles R. Knight; Photograph courtesy Field Museum of Natural History, Chicago.)

EGG-LAYING MAMMALS. The two types which still survive in the Australian region. *Above left*, the duckbill (*Ornithorhynchus*), an amphibious animal with a horny bill and webbed feet. *Above right*, the spiny anteater, with spine-like hair and a long beak, adapted to termite eating. This animal is a powerful digger; the specimen shown (from New Guinea) was able to dig down vertically and bury itself in about one minute. (*Ornithorhynchus*, photograph courtesy New York Zoological Society; *Zaglossus*, photograph by S. D. Ripley.)

POUCHED ANIMALS. The American opossums are the most primitive of living marsupials, but the group survives mainly in Australia. On this page and the three next following are shown a few of the many specialized pouched forms of that continent.

THE TASMANIAN WOLF. An animal which in its habits and almost every major structural feature parallels closely the wolves of other continents, but which, nevertheless, is a true pouched mammal. (From a painting by Charles R. Knight; photograph courtesy American Museum of Natural History, New York.)

THE RABBIT-EARED BANDICOOT. Bandicoots are Australian marsupials which resemble rabbits in their large ears, their hopping ability, and the fact that they dig holes in the ground, but there the resemblance stops; the long nose and long tail are most unrabbit-like and they are insect-eaters rather than vegetarians. (Photograph courtesy New York Zoological Society.)

MARSUPIAL MOTHERS AND YOUNG. *Right* a wallaby with a youngster still in the pouch; *below*, a wombat and its partly grown offspring. The wallabys belong to the kangaroo family. The wombat is a herbivorous form which is in many ways the marsupial 'other number' of the American woodchuck, with rather similar dentition and habits. (Photographs courtesy New York Zoological Society.)

49

GIANT PLEISTOCENE MARSUPIALS. The time of the Ice Age seems to have been that during which mammals reached a peak in size. In Australia there were numerous giant marsupials in the Pleistocene. Two are shown below: a giant kangaroo which may have stood 10 feet high in life and *Diprotodon*, an extinct relative of the wombat, but as large as a rhinoceros. (From a mural by Charles R. Knight; photograph courtesy Field Museum of Natural History, Chicago.)

FLYING PHALANGER. The Australian phalangers are pouched mammals resembling squirrels. To make the comparison closer, we find the development of a 'flying' form (*left*) with parachute folds of skin at the sides of the body like those of the true flying squirrel.

THE KOALA. This Australian animal is frequently termed a native 'bear'. In size, however, it is comparable rather to a Teddy bear, and its habits are not bearlike, for its diet consists of eucalyptus leaves.

THE KANGAROO POUCH. The pouch of a female has been opened up to show two tiny young attached to the mother's teats (Phalanger and koala photographs courtesy New York Zoological Society; pouch photograph by Harry C. Raven.)

THE SHREW. The shrews are the smallest and among the commonest of mammals and represent, most closely of living animals, the insectivorous ancestors of placental mammals. This shy nervous creature is not photogenic; the two figures above, however, give some idea of its appearance (suspicion and defiance appear to be the emotions recorded). (Photographs by Oliver P. Pearson.)

51

INSECTIVORES. *Upper left*, one of the oldest known skulls of a placental mammal, photographed in the hand of its discoverer, Dr Walter Granger, in the Gobi desert. Apart from the shrews, shown overpage, the living insectivores include a number of specialized (rather than primitive) types. *Upper right*, the hedgehog of Europe, a small, prickly, but inoffensive animal (not to be confused with the totally unrelated porcupine). *Lower right*, a mole – an insectivore adapted for underground life and a diet of worms and grubs. The eyes are much reduced, the legs powerful digging instruments. *Lower left*, a tree shrew (*Tupaia*) of the Malay region. The only arboreal insectivores, these animals are closely related to the ancestry of the primates. (Cretaceous skull courtesy American Museum of Natural History, New York, others New York Zoological Society.)

AN ARCHAIC CARNIVORE, or creodont. An Eocene flesh-eating mammal, *Oxyaena*, portrayed as feasting on the tiny dawn horse *Eohippus*. (From a painting by Charles R. Knight, courtesy American Museum of Natural History, New York.)

DOGS. *Left*, *Cynodictis*, a small and primitive form from the Oligocene. Although classed as a dog, this animal may have been close to the stem of all later carnivores. (From Scott, *Land Mammals in the Western Hemisphere*, by permission of the Macmillan Co., publishers.) *Right*, the dingo of Australia, a dog probably introduced into that continent by early men and there run wild; it is similar to some of the domesticated dogs of southern Asia. (Photograph courtesy New York Zoological Society.)

RACCOON RELATIVES. The raccoon is a cousin of the dogs but has kept more closely to a tree-dwelling life and tended toward a mixed or herbivorous diet. Several close relatives of the raccoon are shown here. *Above*, the coati (*Nasua*) of Central and South America, similar in habits to the raccoon but distinguishable by his long nose. *To its right* the true panda (*Ailurus*) of southeastern Asia, a rather larger animal but showing obvious similarities to the raccoon. *Lower right*, a much larger related form (*Ailuropoda*) from the same area, sometimes erroneously called a panda – properly the giant panda. (Photographs courtesy New York Zoological Society.)

53

GIANT BEARS. The largest of bears are related to the large brown bear of Northern Eurasia, represented in the United States by the grizzly bear of the western mountains. The giant of the tribe is the Kadiak bear of the Aleutian Islands of Alaska (*left*), which is reported to reach a weight of 1,400 pounds. Still larger, however, was the great cave bear of the Pleistocene of Europe, illustrated below. (Kadiak bear photograph, courtesy New York Zoological Society; cave bear from a mural by Charles R. Knight; photograph courtesy Field Museum of Natural History, Chicago.)

VARIOUS CARNIVORES:

THE OTTER is a member of the weasel group, which has grown to a moderately good size and taken to an aquatic life as a fish-eater. A close relative, the rare sea otter of the Pacific, has gone farther in this type of life and become a marine form, paralleling the seals.

THE BADGER is also a member of the weasel group and is a powerful digger. The other badger types are found in the Old World.

THE CHEETAH (*Acinonyx*) is an oriental member of the cat family, which is sometimes tamed as a 'hunting dog'. Unlike the typical cats, which depend on a sudden spring to seize their prey, the cheetah is capable of high speed over a long distance.

HYENAS. These are unlovely relatives of the civet-mongoose group of Old World carnivores, which have taken to the life of scavengers. The spotted hyena, shown above, is an African form. Other representatives are the brown hyena of south-west Africa and the striped hyena of north Africa and western Asia. (Hyena photograph courtesy American Museum of Natural History, New York; other photographs courtesy New York Zoological Society.)

PINNIPEDS – AQUATIC CARNIVORES. In several instances mammalian flesh-eaters have taken to an aquatic life. A successful group is that of the Pinnipedia, including the seals, walrus, and their relatives. Above is shown a seal rookery – the Tolstoi rookery on the Pribiloff Islands, Alaska. This is the home of the fur seals of the northern Pacific. The photograph was taken at the height of the breeding season. Families in the background; idle bulls in the foreground. The fur seal and its close relatives the sea lions are found only in the Pacific and are to be distinguished from the common seals of the Atlantic by such features as the absence in the latter of any projecting ear. (Photograph courtesy American Museum of Natural History, New York.)

THE ELEPHANT SEAL (*Macrorhinus*), *above*, in which there is a curious development of a proboscis in the males. This animal is the largest of pinnipeds, attaining a length of 20 feet. It ranges from California to the Antarctic. The photograph (by Sir Douglas Mawson, courtesy New York Zoological Society) shows two bulls fighting on an Antarctic beach.

THE WALRUS (*left*). A ponderous mollusc-eating member of the pinniped group, confined to cold northern seas. The upper canines are enormous tusks which appear to be useful in grubbing for oysters and mussels. (Photograph from a mounted group in the American Museum of Natural History, New York.)

EARLY UNGULATES. *Above*, a restoration of *Phenacodus* of the early Eocene, a very primitive, hoofed mammal type, with all five toes and with teeth of simple structure. *Below*, a scene in the Bridger Basin of southwestern Wyoming in Middle Eocene time. *Right*, large uintatheres, archaic and specialized hoofed forms with three pairs of horns, and, incidentally, small brains. *Left*, *Orohippus*, an early horse type. (From paintings by Charles R. Knight, courtesy American Museum of Natural History, New York, and Field Museum of Natural History, Chicago, respectively.)

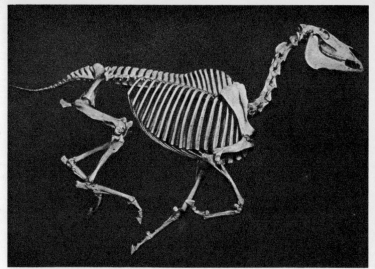

THE SKELETON OF A RACEHORSE (Sysonby), to show some of the features of fast-running ungulates. The proximal joints of the legs are short, giving a powerful drive. The second joint is longer, giving the possibility of a long fore-and-aft swing. The metapodials (bones of palm and sole) are much elongated, giving a third segment to the limb, and the number of toes is reduced. (From a mount by S. H. Chubb in the American Museum of Natural History, New York.)

TAPIRS. These animals have specialized in their rather large size, fairly heavy build, and the development of a protruding nose, but in teeth, feet, and forest-dwelling habits greatly resemble the earliest horses and other primitive odd-toed ungulates (perissodactyls). The form shown here with its young is a South American species; another tapir type is found in the Malay region. (Photograph courtesy New York Zoological Society.)

WESTERN SOUTH DAKOTA IN EARLY OLIGOCENE DAYS. East of the Black Hills of South Dakota is the region known as the Mauvaises Terres, or Big Bad Lands, where much of the country is eroded into a complex series of cliffs and barren ravines which make it bad land indeed for the traveller or rancher but excellent for the fossil collector. The rocks and clays exposed are those of a fairly early period of the Age of Mammals and have yielded a wealth of specimens which have made the region one of the most famous fossil-collecting regions of the world. Above are shown a few of the commonest animals of the early Oligocene of the region. Most spectacular and commonest of fossils in the lower part of the Big Bad Lands deposits are the titanotheres, who in great measure deserve their name of 'titanic mammals'. Large individuals might have a length of about 15 feet, a height at the shoulder of 8 feet. They were related to the horses and rhinoceroses and tended to have the ponderous build of the latter. The peculiar horns, however, are quite unlike those of rhinoceroses and were massive bony structures. The titanotheres appear to have been unprogressive in both teeth and brains and, although very common at the time of this imaginary scene, vanished completely a short time later.

Right, a pair of archaic carnivores (*Hyaenodon*). These may be suspected of having preyed on the titanothere herds by attacking the 'calves'. Left, specimens of a large land tortoise which frequently grew to a yard or more in length of shell; its remains are extremely common in the Bad Lands. (From a mural by Charles R. Knight; photograph courtesy Field Museum of Natural History, Chicago.)

59

HORSES, ancient, 'medieval', and modern. (A series of paintings by Charles R. Knight.) *Top*, the dawn horse (*Eohippus*) of the early Eocene, about fox-terrier size. *Centre, Mesohippus*, a three-toed horse of Oligocene days, about as large as a collie. *Bottom*, Przewalski's horse of the steppes of Asia, the only living wild species of horse. (Photographs courtesy American Museum of Natural History, New York.)

THE ZEBRAS are African forms which, except for their striped skins, are almost indistinguishable from horses and asses. The species shown is Grant's zebra. (Photograph courtesy New York Zoological Society.)

(*Left*) THE INDIAN RHINOCEROS. A young female in which the horn is not developed, but its swollen bony base is visible over the nose. The Indian and Javan rhinoceroses are one-horned and with a folded skin resembling armour; other living rhinos of Africa and Sumatra are two-horned and with a smoother skin. (Photograph courtesy New York Zoological Society.)

(*Bottom*) AN EXTINCT RUNNING RHINOCEROS, *Hyracodon* of the Oligocene. Early rhinoceroses were hornless and often rather slimly built and comparable to their cousins, the horses, in general appearance. (A restoration by Charles R. Knight; photograph courtesy American Museum of Natural History, New York.)

THE LARGEST LAND ANIMAL. *Baluchitherium*, a giant, hornless, fossil rhinoceros of the Oligocene of Asia, is the largest animal known which was a land dweller. It is, of course, exceeded in size by some whales, and some of the sauropod dinosaurs (as *Brontosaurus*) were larger but were obviously not true land forms. *Baluchitherium* specimens vary somewhat in size; the largest known individual appears to have been about 17 feet high at the shoulder and 27 feet in length. The skull was about 5 feet long but was (as may be seen from the restoration) rather small for the animal. (Restoration by Mrs E. R. Fulda; photographs courtesy American Museum of Natural History, New York.)

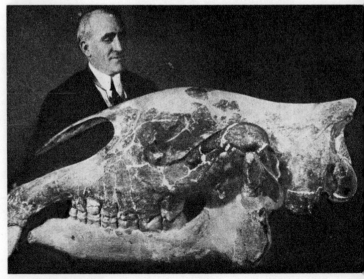

THE WESTERN PLAINS IN EARLY MIOCENE DAYS, about the middle of the Age of Mammals. In the foreground a group of giant hogs (*Dinohyus*), one of which is digging up roots for food (a habit suggested by the signs of wear on their teeth). These forms are but distantly related to the true hogs. An average individual would have had a height of about 6 feet. *Right*, a pair of chalicotheres (*Moropus*), ungainly odd-toed 'ungulates', which despite their relationships to horses, etc., have powerful claws rather than hoofs. The claws indicate that they may have dug for tubers; on the other hand, the long legs and neck suggest that they browsed from tree branches as shown in the painting. *Left*, a pair of rhinoceroses (*Diceratherium*), peculiar in that the horns were arranged side by side on the nose. Behind them, contemporary small three-toed horses (*Parahippus*) and in the background a group of slender gazelle camels (*Stenomylus*). Remains of animals of this age are abundant in northwestern Nebraska particularly at the famous Agate Springs quarry on the Niobrara River. (From a mural by Charles R. Knight; by permission of the Field Museum of Natural History, Chicago.)

PIGLIKE UNGULATES. The swine are the characteristic members of a sub-order of even-toed ungulates, the Suina, in which the cud-chewing habit of the ruminants is not developed and in which the feet have typically four well-developed toes.

In America the pigs are represented by the peccaries, not uncommon in the tropics and found as far north as Texas. They are distinguished by the fact that the upper tusks (canine teeth) are not curved upward as they are in the true pigs.

The babirussa is a peculiar pig from the Celebes in which these upper tusks are highly specialized; they force their way upward through the roof of the snout and curve backward so far that their utility as weapons is much reduced.

The hippopotamus is a lubberly amphibious relative of the swine. In addition to the familiar large hippopotamus (seen asking for a peanut, *top right*), there is a pygmy hippopotamus in Liberia. At the bottom left is an adult female of this species and her offspring. (Photographs courtesy New York Zoological Society.)

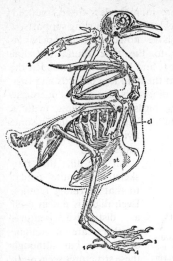

The skeleton of a modern bird. Note the huge breastbone, the short body, and tail. The wing skeleton includes the remains of the first three 'fingers'. The foot is four toed, with the first toe at the back, the second to fourth pointed forward, with a structure very similar to that of many dinosaurs. The bird 'wishbone' is the collarbone, or clavicle (*cl*), of other animals. The enormous breastbone, or sternum (*st*), is developed to carry the powerful wing muscles (the 'whitemeat' of the chicken). (After Heilmann, *The Origin of Birds*, by permission of D. Appleton - Century Co., publishers)

rendered essential the care and feeding of the fledgelings in the nest.

Brain and sense organs are much modified in relation to flight. Birds (like men, but in contrast to most other vertebrates) depend largely upon their eyes for their information about the outside world. The eyes are large; within the eyeball is a circle of bony plates. Such plates are present in many primitive vertebrates as a protection against water pressure; here the protection is against wind pressure in flight. The brain is very much larger than in reptiles, but the increase seems to be related not so much to general intelligence as to the development of the centres having to do with sight, balance, and the delicate muscular co-ordinations necessary in flying. In the skeleton there are many modifications in connexion with flight. With the result of lessening the specific gravity, not only are there air sacs within the body connected with the lungs, but many of the bones of the skeleton are hollow and air-filled.

The breastbone, or sternum, is usually little developed in reptiles; in birds it is an enormous plate covering nearly the whole underside of the chest, with a strong keel in the midline. To it are attached the powerful chest muscles propelling the wings (these muscles form the white meat of the chicken). In the hand there are but three fingers remaining of the original five (there has been a similar reduction in some dinosaurs), and these are more or less fused, reduced, and clawless, acting as wing supports.

We have noted that the pelvis is similar to the type found in some dinosaurs and have also mentioned the fact that the hind legs of birds and two-footed dinosaurs are almost identical. Modern birds are toothless, with a horny bill, a feature also found in some flying reptiles and dinosaurs.

All in all, the bird skeleton is quite similar to that of ruling reptiles. Even flight is not in itself a distinctive feature. Feathers are a unique character; but although these structures seem quite different from the horny scales which cover a reptile's body, the difference is in reality not very great. The two are identical

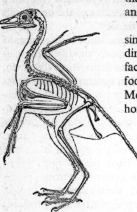

Skeleton of one of the oldest known birds, *Archaeornis*. If this be compared with the recent bird shown in the last figure, the main differences noted here are the long bony tail, the clawed fingers, and the absence of the great keeled breastbone. All these are characters in which the oldest birds were still reptilian and dinosaur-like in nature. (After Heilmann, *The Origin of Birds*, by permission of D. Appleton – Century Co., publishers)

in chemical composition; feathers may have come from horny scales in which the edges have developed into a large number of fine, interlocking subdivisions.

THE OLDEST-KNOWN BIRDS. The description given above applies to the typical modern bird. Far different in many respects and much closer to their archosaur ancestors were the oldest-known birds, *Archaeopteryx* and *Archaeornis* of the Jurassic. Skeletons of these two primitive birds have been found in the lithographic stone deposits mentioned in the last chapter. It is fortunate that the delicate type of preservation characteristic of these beds has shown traces of the feathers, for otherwise there is little to distinguish these early forms from some of the small dinosaurs. The tail was still of the old-fashioned reptilian type but with a double row of feathers down its length; there were wings, but these were rather feeble, and the three fingers supporting them still bore claws. The breastbone was small, indicating weak flying muscles. None of the bones was hollow, and the jaws were armed with teeth. These forms are, because of the possession of feathers, technically birds, but birds not far removed from their ruling-reptile forebears.

There has been much discussion as to the origin of flight. The theory most generally held is that the ancestral bird was a tree dweller and that flight started as a slight parachute effect as the

Skeletons of Cretaceous toothed birds. *Left, Ichthyornis*, the 'fish bird', a small form about 8 inches in height, with good powers of flight. *Right, Hesperornis*, the 'western bird', a large wingless diver. These skeletons were found in the 1870's (when the woodcuts here reproduced were made). Curiously, but little further material of these interesting birds has since been discovered. (From Marsh)

Proavis jumped from branch to branch, the developing wings breaking the fall on landing; gliding would have been a subsequent stage. A second theory is that the ancestors were ground types and that the feathered arms and tail helped, by acting as planes, to increase the speed in running, lifting the Proavis somewhat off the ground.

CRETACEOUS AND LATER BIRDS. A full period after the appearance of the first birds we catch a second glimpse of the developing bird life of the Age of Reptiles in the remains of some water birds from the marine rocks of Kansas. One of the types, *Hesperornis*, the 'western bird', was a water-dwelling diver which had lost the power of flight; a second, *Ichthyornis*, the 'fish bird', seems to have lived a life like that of modern terns. In both forms teeth were present, but the fish bird was already highly modernized in most other respects, with powerfully developed wings. Teeth appear to have been lost at about the end of the Mesozoic, and during the Tertiary there took place the development of modern bird groups.

Concerning most of these we shall have but little to say here. Birds are intensely interesting to many of us because of their plumage, habits, and songs. But the classification of the group presents relatively little of interest to the scientist, for under their skins birds are remarkably uniform in structure. Their fossil history is very poorly known; their small and hollow bones are preserved only rarely. We shall, however, mention here a few of the more primitive or more aberrant types of birds.

FLIGHTLESS BIRDS. To-day we find in the southern continents a number of flightless types of birds – the rhea of South America, the ostrich of Africa, the emu and cassowary of the Australian region, and the kiwi of New Zealand. In the Pleistocene epoch just behind us there were several other birds of the same sort, notably the 'elephant birds' of Madagascar, whose enormous eggs have sometimes been found preserved entire in the swamps of that island, and the varied moas of New Zealand (one reaching a dozen feet in height), which seem to have been still in existence when the Maoris reached those islands not so many centuries ago. Except for the kiwi, all these birds have much in common; they are large, with powerful hind legs and small heads, the wings have been reduced to vestiges, and the feathers are soft and fluffy. Many workers have suggested that these birds are primitive types which had never attained the power of flight. The similarities, however, are merely features which one would expect in any sort of large bird which had ceased to fly. Their distribution is interesting. Considerable freedom from enemies is a feature common to these types. In New Zealand there is not a single flesh-eater to disturb them. In Australia the only carnivores are comparatively harmless pouched animals related to the opossums; there were (in nature) no members of the cat or wolf tribes on that continent. The same was also true of South America until quite recent geological times, and the island of Madagascar has no flesh-eaters of any great size. Further, the rhea and ostrich dwell in open country where, once they attain any size and speed, escape from enemies is easy.

All these facts suggest that these great ground-dwelling birds are really descended from flying types, although probably from forms in which flight was poorly developed. Why do birds fly at all? The search for food is a major factor; but safety from enemies is perhaps a still more important reason. If regions could be found where food were plentiful enough without flying for it and where there were no enemies of importance, birds might well abandon flying, conserve their energies, and return to the ground. Such conditions are met with in the homes of most of these flightless types and may have been responsible for the development of the Pleistocene and Recent giant birds.

Flightless birds, although of a quite different sort, were present in the early Tertiary of the Americas. *Diatryma*, a fossil wingless bird from Wyoming, was a contemporary of the earliest horses. The horse, at that time, was the size of a fox terrier; this bird was seven feet tall.

These giant early birds arouse one to speculation; their presence suggests some interesting possibilities – which never materialized. At the end of the Mesozoic, as we have seen, the great reptiles died off. The surface of the earth was open for conquest. As possible successors there were two groups, the mammals – our own relatives – and the birds. The former group succeeded, but the presence of such forms as *Diatryma* shows that the birds were, at the beginning, their rivals. What would the earth be like to-day had the birds won and the mammals vanished?

PENGUINS. We cannot leave the topic of bird oddities without a brief mention of the penguins. These solemn-looking fellows are primitive in some respects but in others are among the most highly specialized of birds. The wings are totally incapable of functioning in flight but are powerful flippers used in swimming.

The penguins are confined to the Southern Hemisphere, and remains of fossil penguins (some as large as a man) have been found in deposits on southern islands dating to the dawn of the Tertiary. An interesting suggestion has been put forward as to their origin. When the mammals, at that time, succeeded to the crown of the reptiles over most of the earth, it is possible that members of this class did not reach the isolated Antarctic land areas. This empty continent would have presented an excellent opportunity for the ancestral penguins to return to a ground life much as many other birds have done in other regions. But while the Antarctic appears to have then had a temperate climate, there must soon have begun in Antarctica, as elsewhere, the gradual cooling of the polar regions which was to reach a peak in the Pleistocene Ice Age. With the loss of flight, these birds could not escape by air from an isolated and increasingly inhospitable land. Escape into the sea, however, was still possible. Such may have been the history of the penguins.

HOMING AND MIGRATIONS. It is a matter of common knowledge that many birds are able to return to their nests even if removed to a considerable distance; the homing pigeon is a familiar example of this, and all birds which have been investigated exhibit the homing instinct to a greater or lesser degree. Of course, not all birds taken far from their nests return; some may be in poor condition and unable to make the flight; others may become victims of enemies or of storms; others possibly may not strongly feel the 'urge' to return even if capable of doing so. But a remarkably large percentage do return, and return promptly.

How this is accomplished is a scientific mystery. A bird may learn a route, as is the case in training homing pigeons, or, even if taken over it only once, might pick up enough visual landmarks. But vision can be eliminated as a necessary feature. Birds can still return if carried away blindfolded or if transported by sea, as, for example, terns taken by boat from Key West across the entire Gulf of Mexico to Galveston. Perhaps, one might suggest, the bird can, in default of vision, be able to keep track of the direction in which it is travelling, just as a man can to a degree maintain his orientation when travelling at night by keeping account of the turns of the road. But this possibility has been eliminated by carrying birds long distances (as Berlin to Frankfort on the Main) strapped to a revolving phonograph turntable. Such birds, apart from a touch of understandable dizziness, appear to be quite undismayed and have promptly returned home.

A final (although fairly obvious) suggestion is that their return is a matter of chance; released, they simply wander about and may eventually strike the right spot. But here a time factor enters. It is obvious, from simple geometry, that, if one bird is taken twice as far from home as another, its return by random wandering should take about four times as long, on the average. This is not the case. Such returned birds take only about twice as long; and in returns in general the time consumed is merely a reasonable one for a direct flight.

We have thus exhausted all reasonable possibilities of explaining this remarkable instinct. Recently a psychologist wishing to do more work on this problem applied for financial support to a fund designed for the investigation of psychic phenomena. Such phenomena, it was decreed, were to be defined as those beyond the realm of the known senses. The investigator argued that the homing instinct was in this category as surely as anything he knew of! His request was refused, but his argument seems to us a reasonable one.

Equally interesting is the topic of migration. In North Temperate zones we see each autumn a vast streaming southward of the bird population and each spring an equally great series of northward migrations. Why do birds migrate and how are these migrations, often over long and complicated routes, accomplished?

It has been suggested that an annual north-and-south drifting of bird populations began in the late Tertiary as climatic conditions, previously rather uniform over much of the earth, became sharply zoned (as at present) between arctic and tropics and marked seasonal differences became established. This does not, however, tell us why an individual bird to-day migrates, for the bird is not versed in geological history, nor can it read a calendar. What sets off the migratory stimulus? Temperature, perhaps, or light? Will cold weather or shorter days send a bird southward, and vice versa?

Research appears to rule out temperature as a factor, but the length of day appears to be influential, in some cases as least. Seasons of migration and breeding seasons are closely connected; and the lights seen burning in many a farmer's henhouse on winter evenings are a demonstration that light and reproductive activities are closely associated. Increased amounts of light seem to stimulate the pituitary gland (apparently via the eye); this gland in turn stimulates the gonads (resulting in the case of the fowl in more eggs). In many birds lengthening days (and hence more light) are followed by migration and breeding. The breeding is associated with light supply. May not the migration be equally associated? Such work as has been done suggests that this is the case, although the results are not conclusive.

But even if we find a mechanism for setting off the migratory impulse, we have not solved the entire problem. For in many cases the migration is no mere drifting north and south, but one which follows definite paths. The Alaskan golden plover in autumn sets its course southward over three thousand miles of open ocean to the Hawaiian Islands on its way to the South Seas. How does it set so straight a course, when a deviation of a few degrees would cause it to miss its goal?

The more common American golden plover follows a more complicated route. Following a June nesting season on the Arctic shores of north-western Canada, the adult birds fly east to spend the early autumn in Labrador. Then, turning southward, they take a straight course from Newfoundland and Nova Scotia to Venezuela, never normally touching land unless driven off their course by storms. A further, more leisurely, migration carries them to centre in the Paraguay region by the time winter has arrived in the North.

Possibly a bird might learn such a route by following his elders. But what of the newly hatched young? They are left behind in the Arctic; there is no one to guide them. A month later they leave and follow the same complicated route east to Labrador, south over the ocean to the Orinoco, and, finally, after some six thousand miles of travel over lands and seas they had never seen, rejoin the older birds in their wintering region. Why and how do they do this, all untaught? Does each germ cell of the golden plover carry within its tiny nucleus a marked flying chart of the Western Hemisphere?

CHAPTER 8

Varied Reptilian Types

IN THE present chapter there will be considered briefly several reptilian groups which have had less spectacular careers than the ruling reptiles but which have been, nevertheless, successful in surviving to the present time; in addition we shall treat of two extinct types of interesting marine reptiles.

SCALED REPTILES

LIZARDS. The lizards are a comparatively unprogressive but yet not an unsuccessful group. They are the most abundant of living reptiles, represented in the tropical and warmer temperate regions by a host of genera and species. They have in great measure retained the primitive sprawling type of walking characteristic of primitive land dwellers and the salamanders. The limbs, however, are lightly built, and some lizard types are capable of running rapidly. The average lizard is a small form; but on the island of Komodo in the East Indies there are living monitor lizards attaining a length of about a dozen feet. One fossil lizard from the Pleistocene of Asia was at least twice as long, thus reaching the proportions of many dinosaurs.

There are numerous interesting variants of the lizard group. The chameleon of the Old World tropics is a grotesque creature with a long protrusible tongue for insect-catching and a clutching hand which has, not a thumb opposed to the remaining four fingers, but two fingers opposed to the other three. Some burrowing lizards, again, have become blind and are limbless, in snakelike fashion.

MARINE LIZARDS. We have reviewed the various stages through which the ancestors of the reptiles passed to be completely freed from an aquatic existence and become purely land-dwelling types. But, curiously, no sooner did the reptiles attain this terrestrial mode of life than many groups began to reverse the process and return to the water. We have noted that among the ruling reptiles the phytosaurs and crocodiles had returned to an amphibious type of existence, and also among the lizards several groups have become water dwellers.

The one living marine lizard to-day is a form found on the Galápagos Islands. It is an excellent swimmer, using a long compressed tail as a propulsive organ and feeding upon the seaweeds along the shore. This lizard, however, is not completely adapted for water life (its toes, e.g., are only partly webbed) and spends most of its existence upon the shores. Much more highly adapted to a marine existence were the mosasaurs, huge marine lizards of the Cretaceous. These great extinct forms are found in marine deposits in almost every region of the earth; the best skeletons have been obtained from the chalk rocks of the seas which once covered western Kansas. The name, however, derives from the fact that the first specimen came from the banks of the Meuse River (Latin *Mosa*) in Holland, whence it was taken to Paris in 1795 as one of the major spoils of a French revolutionary army campaign.

The large mosasaurs reached a maximum length of thirty to forty feet; about half the length was included in the long flattened tail, which was obviously the main swimming organ. The limbs were very short, with broad spreading toes which presumably were webbed in life and served a steering function. The numerous pointed teeth of the typical mosasaurs lead us to believe that they subsisted on fish, plentiful remains of which are present in the same deposits.

SNAKES. A development from the lizard stock is that of the snakes, last evolved and most progressive of living reptiles. Lizards are not known before the Jurassic, and the snakes do not appear until the Cretaceous, last of the periods of the Age of Reptiles.

A snake is a logical outcome of lizard evolutionary history. We have noted before that the early land animals, like their fish ancestors before them, depended in great measure upon a sinuous twisting of the trunk in locomotion, the small limbs mainly acting as supports against which a forward push could be exerted. The snakes use the same principle but have abandoned legs and utilize their scales as points of support. The thick horny scales with which they as well as their lizard cousins are covered overlap shingle fashion with their free margins pointing backward. As the body twists the scales prevent any backslip but offer no opposition to forward movement.

Some lizards unrelated to snake ancestry, we have noted, had also lost their legs; the true distinctive feature of the snakes is the much modified skull. In the snake the jaws are readily spread apart and are very loosely attached to the skull so that the gape of the mouth is enormous; a snake but a few feet long can swallow a rabbit entire and digest it at leisure; some tropical snakes can swallow a man.

The skull of a python to show some of the mechanisms for swallowing large objects. The two jaw halves are loosely connected; the front bone of the lower jaw (*d*) can be bent on the back part of the jaw (*sa*). In addition to the ordinary movement of the jaw joint the two bones above this region (*q*, *sq*) can also be moved on the skull; the front part of the skull is also flexible. The teeth are directed backward; any motion tends to push a seized object down the throat, and it cannot slip outward.

Only one lizard (the Gila monster) is poisonous, and even among snakes the majority are quite harmless; in most of the United States, for example, the rattlesnake and copperhead (and the water moccasin in the South) are the only noxious forms. The poison is developed in sacs adjacent to certain of the teeth in the upper jaw, usually a pair near the front of the mouth. In some cases these teeth have a groove down one edge through which the poison may trickle into the wound; in the more highly developed forms the tooth is hollow, exactly analogous to a hypodermic needle in construction.

THE TUATERA. Living to-day only on a few isolated islets off the coast of New Zealand is the tuatera, scientifically known as *Sphenodon*, a small reptile which appears superficially much like the lizards and resembles that group also in many structural features. There are, however, some characters more primitive than those of any lizard; in the temple region, for example, there are two perforations in the bones roofing the skull and giving play to the jaw muscles. The lizards appear to have lost one of these temple openings, but both have been retained in the skull of ruling reptiles. It was long ago pointed out that the tuatera is a reptilian 'missing link' which may be a survivor of an archaic group from which the ruling reptiles, lizards, and perhaps other types may have evolved. Strong evidence for this point of view lies in the fact that forms quite similar to *Sphenodon* are found as fossils in rocks far back in the Age of Reptiles.

Why has this 'living fossil' survived in this one locality when its relatives have otherwise perished? This is an extreme case of survival due to isolation. Archaic members of any group usually persist only when comparatively free from competition with more progressive types. New Zealand has probably been completely separated from other bodies of land since some time in the Age of Reptiles. The development of mammals in other continents has probably been a factor in the destruction of the tuatera's relatives over most of the world. But not a single mammal (except the bats) appears to have reached New Zealand until man arrived, and the lack of competition has presumably been the reason for the preservation of this archaic reptile.

TURTLES

The turtles are the most bizarre of reptilian groups. Because they are still living, turtles are commonplace objects to us; were they extinct, their shells, the most remarkable armour ever assumed by a land animal, would be a cause for wonder.

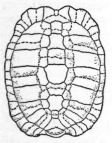

Diagram of the upper shell, or carapace, of a turtle. The major structure consists of plates of bone, outlined in continuous line. These consist of a middle row of plates, one over each joint of the backbone; paired rows of rib plates on each side; and a marginal row encircling the whole. These bones, however, are invisible in the living turtle, for they are covered by horny scutes, the outlines of which are in broken lines in the diagram. Note that in most cases the joints of the two types of covering alternate, thus strengthening the structure.

THE SHELL. The armour plate of an ordinary modern turtle is composed of two materials – horny scutes representing the ordinary reptilian scales on the surface and bony plates underneath. The outlines of these two sets of armour materials do not in general coincide; there is an alternation of joints, which gives greater strength to the combined structure.

The shell is divided into upper and lower portions (carapace and plastron, respectively), connected by a bridge at the sides. Down the middle of the top is a row of almost square bony plates, most of which are fused tightly to the joints of the backbone beneath them; on either side is a row of longer plates fused to the corresponding ribs; a ring of small plates around the margin completes the top shield. The undershield is composed of a much smaller number of large plates. The shell is widely opened at the front for the withdrawal of the head and front legs, behind for the hind legs and stubby tail.

The turtle gait is a very awkward and lumbering one, with the limbs sprawled outward at the side. With the broad ventral shield no other type of walking is, of course, possible. But it is probable that this style of walking antedates the construction of the turtle's shell. This sort of locomotion was, we have noted, characteristic of primitive land dwellers in general. Apparently the turtles evolved their shells before styles in walking had improved; once the armour was in place, no improvement was possible.

In turtles (as in modern birds) the teeth have been entirely lost and replaced by a stout and sharp horny bill bounding the margins of the jaws.

TURTLE TYPES. Most primitive of living turtles are a few forms, unfamiliar to most of us, which dwell in the southern continents. The original turtles, it would seem, had not the power of drawing in their necks. These 'side-necked' turtles (pleurodires) of South America, Africa, and the East Indies have solved the problem of head protection by tucking their necks sideways over their shoulders under the front edge of the shield.

All other turtles, including all those found in the northern continents, have evolved a different mode of head protection. In these forms (the cryptodires or 'concealed necks') the head is drawn straight back into the shell, the neck being very flexible and bending into an S-shaped curve when the head is pulled back.

Some turtles are normal land dwellers, this being particularly true of the high-shelled tortoises. Some members of this group, such as the ordinary 'hard-shelled gopher' of the southern United States, are rather small forms, but on various islands such as the Galápagos and Mauritius they grow to gigantic size. Very probably this growth is related to the absence of enemies on the islands. Reptiles in general do not reach any definite adult size but continue to grow, albeit slowly, throughout life, and some of these ponderous tortoises appear to be a century or two old.

AQUATIC TURTLES. The trend towards an aquatic existence is strong in the turtles. The various types of marsh and mud turtles spend, as their names imply, much of their time in the water, and the snappers and the soft-shelled turtles are stream dwellers. Even farther along this line of development are several purely marine types of turtles which spend almost their entire life at sea, coming ashore only to lay their eggs. Since the body is inflexible and the tail but stubby, locomotion is necessarily a function of the legs alone, which are short broad paddles with the toes webbed.

The armour is of reduced importance to a water dweller and, furthermore, is a considerable hindrance, since it increases the specific gravity of the animal. In the soft-shelled river turtles

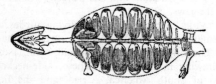

The skeleton (incompletely known) of a small fossil reptile (*Eunotosaurus*) from the Permian, which may be related to the ancestry of the turtles. Eight pairs of the ribs are expanded into broad bony plates; this may represent the beginning of the turtle carapace. (From Watson)

the horny scutes have been lost, and the same is true of one sea turtle, the leatherback. The other living sea forms, the green (turtle soup!), hawksbill, and loggerhead turtles, have retained the horny covering but have lost most of the underlying armour.

This last condition was also true of the oldest known sea turtles which were present in the Cretaceous seas as contemporaries of the mosasaurs. These were in some instances very large forms, one having a body a dozen feet in length.

TURTLE HISTORY. The exact line of descent of turtles from the stem reptiles is not certain. A clue, however, is afforded by the finding in the Permian rocks of South Africa of a small animal with a long name, *Eunotosaurus*, which has broadly expanded ribs, giving it somewhat the appearance of an umbrella plant and suggesting the beginning of the turtle shell.

The turtles, once within the shelter of their armour, became the conservatives of the reptilian world. The oldest forms were contemporaries of the earliest dinosaurs. The ruling reptiles grew to dominate the reptilian scene, but the turtles persisted unchanged. The dinosaurs passed away, and the mammals took their place, but the turtles went calmly on their placid way. Now man dominates the scene, but the turtles are still with us. And if, in the far distant future, man in turn disappears from the earth, very likely there will still be found the turtle plodding stolidly on down the corridor of time.

PLESIOSAURS

We have observed that marine branches have developed in several groups of reptiles which have also terrestrial representatives. We shall conclude this chapter with a consideration of two extinct reptilian groups which were exclusively marine in nature.

The oldest remains of one of these groups, the plesiosaurs, came to light in Europe over a century ago. The scientific name applied then to them means 'near reptiles' and refers to the fact that it was then thought that they were forms coming up towards the reptilian

The limbs of various aquatic reptiles. *D*, a fairly primitive type of reptile, little adapted to marine life. Of this form only the foot is drawn; in the other figures the entire limb is shown, the long joints shortening up to make a compact paddle. *A* and *B* are ichthyosaurs (*Merriamia* and *Ophthalmosaurus*) in which the number of toe joints has been considerably increased, while in *B* extra toes have been added. In the plesiosaurs, as in *C* (*Elasmosaurus*), there are always five toes, but the number of joints may be much increased. In the marine lizards, as in *E* (*Clidastes*), the toes are fairly normal but were spread out and were presumably webbed. (Mainly after Williston)

level from a former water-dwelling life. We now know, however, that the reverse was really the case and that they are, again, descendants of land animals which had taken to the seas and adopted a fish-eating mode of existence.

The plesiosaurs were common inhabitants of the Jurassic oceans and survived until near the close of the Cretaceous, where they are found as contemporaries of the marine lizards and earliest sea turtles. Plesiosaurs reached a maximum length of about forty feet, and one form from Australia had a skull nearly ten feet in length, a size record for reptiles. Their build was a curious one. An old writer described a plesiosaur as 'a snake strung through the body of a turtle', and in some instances the comparison is not inapt. The trunk was very broad, flat, and inflexible and was well plated with bones. These, however, were not armour but areas for attachment of the powerful muscles of the paddles. Since the trunk was a rigid structure and the tail little developed, the plesiosaurs, like the similarly constructed turtles, had to 'row' themselves along by powerfully developed limbs. These were much more highly specialized than the limbs of lizards, for the number of joints was often greatly increased. In no normal land reptile does the number of joints in a toe exceed five at the outside; in plesiosaurs there were sometimes over a dozen joints per toe.

An unwieldy body of this sort was obviously a disadvantageous structure for animals which pursued elusive fishes; sharp turns and delicate steering were as impossible as they are in a rowboat. In compensation we find that many plesiosaurs had much elongated and flexible necks (one form had seventy-two neck vertebrae!) which could be readily turned to dart the head at the prey. Such forms usually had short heads; another type of plesiosaur had a shorter neck but a much-elongated beak which appeared to serve just as well.

ICHTHYOSAURS

Of all reptiles, the group most highly adapted to an aquatic existence was that of the extinct ichthyosaurs, which well deserve their name of 'fish reptiles'. The life-span of these forms covered most of the Mesozoic, or Age of Reptiles; they seem to have occupied the place in nature now taken by the dolphins and porpoises.

The superficial appearance was very fishlike; the body was short and rather deep and compressed laterally; the neck was very short, with the head set closely on the shoulders, so that there was a reappearance of the torpedo-like fish type in body form. In black shales in southern Germany have been found a number of specimens in which the skin outline has been preserved. These specimens show that there was a large fishlike dorsal fin. Even more interesting is the tail construction. Early finds all showed an apparently broken tail with the end of the backbone sagging downwards. The older restorations 'corrected' this and showed a normal straight-tailed animal. But specimens with the body

The tail in ichthyosaurs. *Left*, a Triassic form (*Mixosaurus*) with a comparatively primitive sort of tail; the end of the backbone is turned slightly downward. *Right*, an advanced ichthyosaur with a superficially sharklike tail, the end of the vertebral column tilted downward. (After Wiman)

outlines preserved prove that the seeming break is a normal condition; there was a very sharklike tail with, however, the backbone extending down into the lower lobe, whereas in fishes it tilts upwards into the upper half of the fin.

The ichthyosaurs undoubtedly swam in fishlike fashion by lateral undulations of body and tail, and the limbs, used only for steering and balancing, are comparatively small. They are very highly modified; the individual bones assumed circular or polygonal contours and were packed very closely together so that while the limb as a whole was flexible, there were no free movements between the joints. As in the plesiosaurs, there was a considerable increase in the number of toe joints. But while the plesiosaurs retained the original number of toes, the fish reptiles varied widely. Some had but three toes in a fin; in others, new toes were budded off, giving as many as eight digits; this is the only group of four-footed animals which has exceeded the orthodox number of toes.

These creatures were so extreme in their marine adaptations and their limbs so obviously unsuited for use on land that the problem of ichthyosaur reproduction was early raised. A reptile's egg will drown in the water as surely as an adult. In some snakes and lizards the eggs are retained in the mother's body until they hatch, and it was suggested that the reproduction of ichthyosaurs must have been of a similar nature. In agreement with this idea that the fish reptile's young were born alive are a number of specimens which actually show skeletons of young ichthyosaurs inside the body of an adult individual. It has been argued that these may have been youngsters which had been eaten by mistake. But in several instances the young have been observed partially emergent from what would have been the outer opening of the reproductive tract in life. The mother here apparently died during childbirth or (there are human parallels) labour may have taken place after the death of the mother.

CHAPTER 9

The Origin of Mammals

WE now retrace our steps from a consideration of the great dynasties of the Age of Reptiles to the origin of our own closer relatives. Man is a mammal, member of a great group which includes almost all the larger animals inhabiting the surface of the earth (to say nothing of the whales and seals of the seas, the bats in the air).

MAMMAL CHARACTERS

REPRODUCTION. The name indicates one of the features of the group. Mammals nurse their young. Postnatal care of the young is unusual in lower vertebrates but common in birds and mammals, highest of backboned animals. In addition, none but the most primitive of mammals lays eggs; all others bear their young alive, and in most there is a well-developed mechanism for the nourishment of the young embryo within the mother's body. All these features seem to be associated with a high degree of organization of the mammal body, for the development of which there is needed a considerable period of growth.

WARM BLOOD. Mammals are warm-blooded forms; a high body temperature is maintained. Hair and sweat glands are peculiar mammalian features associated with temperature regulation, and there is a highly developed breathing mechanism which is in constant use. In addition there is a very efficient circulatory system with a complete separation of aerated and impure blood streams. The heart (pp. 338, 343) is a double-barrelled, four-chambered organ, as in birds (but not in reptiles), with blood on one side in transit from the body to the lungs, on the other, from the lungs to the body.

BRAINS. The brain of reptiles is a small structure tucked away in a small area at the base of the skull. The brain of mammals, even the most stupid of them, has enlarged enormously. Most parts of the brain have, however, remained fairly constant in size. It is in the cerebral hemispheres, originally small structures dedicated to the sense of smell, that almost all the growth has taken place. Here there have arisen higher brain centres which have placed the mammals as a group far above any other vertebrate stock in their degree of mental development.

SKULL. The skull and head of mammals is a very different structure from that of reptiles. Many of the reptile bones have been lost (cf. p. 363), and the pineal eye no longer functions. The originally solid temporal region has been pierced for the accommodation of the jaw muscles, leaving a bar, or arch, at the edge of the cheek region; the brain case has swollen out enormously to accommodate the expanding brain. The skull of reptiles joins the backbone by a single, round, bony knob, or condyle; in mammals a pair of condyles is present. In reptiles (except the crocodiles) the nostrils open into the front of the mouth. In mammals there has developed a bony partition which separates nasal and food passages back to the throat, a feature of importance in forms in which constant breathing is a vital necessity. In reptiles there are normally some seven bones in the lower jaw; we mammals have but one (the dentary), and this articulates with a different bone on the side of the skull, the squamosal. Our whole joint has changed.

TEETH. The dentition of mammals has become greatly modified. Lower vertebrates have an indefinite amount of tooth replacement; mammals have but two sets of teeth, 'milk'

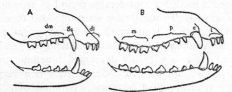

The teeth of a generalized mammal (primitive placental) seen from the right side. *A*, deciduous ('milk') teeth, consisting of incisors (*di*), canines (*dc*), and 'milk molars' (*dm*); *B*, permanent teeth, including incisors (*i*), canines (*c*), and premolars (*p*) replacing the milk teeth, and, in addition, the permanent molars (*m*).

and permanent. The teeth of primitive vertebrates were usually of about the same shape in different parts of the jaw; in mammals the various parts of the tooth row are highly differentiated. There was some early variation, but in the ancestors of the higher mammals the dentition came to be made up of three sharp nipping teeth, or incisors, at the front of each half of each jaw, a single large, stout, piercing tusk, the canine, four premolar teeth behind this in the front of the cheek region, and three grinders, the molars. This gives a total of forty-four teeth. Most mammals have lost some of this set of teeth (we have, e.g., but thirty-two); few have exceeded this number. This type of dentition is one suitable for a carnivore, and the ancestry of all the mammals lies through a long line of flesh-eating types.

EARS. In reptiles the eardrum lies almost at the surface, near the back of the jaws; in mammals it is deeply sunk in a tube, and an external ear flap for the concentration of sound waves has made its appearance. In reptiles there is but one small ossicle, the stapes, for the transmission of sound from drum to inner ear; in mammals there are three. As we shall see (cf. chap. 17), the two new ossicles have been derived from the old reptile jaw joint.

LOCOMOTION IN MAMMALS. We have discussed the cumbersome, waddling type of walking common to all primitive land animals and noted how the ruling reptiles solved the 'problem' of fast movement by taking to a bipedal mode of life. Our ancestors also came to a successful solution, but in quite another way. All four limbs were retained but swung around into a fore-and-aft position, the knees brought forward, the elbows back. In this mammalian pose, we have a much more efficient sort of apparatus than the primitive one. In an early reptile type much of the energy expended was used to keep the body from collapsing on the limbs; here all the muscles can be used for straightaway forward propulsion. This change in posture has been accompanied by many changes in the bones and muscles of the limbs, of which we will note but one feature here. In primitive reptiles the count of the toe joints was, from the 'thumb' or big toe out, 2-3-4-5-3; in mammals the middle fingers have shortened up, giving a count of 2-3-3-3-3 (p. 373).

ACTION. If we attempt to evaluate the meaning of all the features in the structure of mammals which distinguish them from reptiles, we may perhaps sum them up in one word – activity. The ancestors of the mammals were carnivores, leading lives in which speedy locomotion was a necessity. The limb development has given effectiveness to this potential activity. Brain growth has given it intelligent direction. The maintenance of a high body temperature and the various changes associated with this are related to the need of a continuous supply of energy in animals leading a constantly active life. Even the improvements in reproductive habits, which are a prominent feature of mammalian development, seem related to the needs for a slow maturation of the complex mechanisms (particularly the brain) upon which the successful pursuit of an alert and active life depends.

OUR REPTILIAN ANCESTORS

We might at first imagine that the evolution of such a highly developed group as the mammals would have been a late feature in reptilian history. This, however, is exactly the reverse of the case. The reptilian stem from which the mammals sprang was one of the first differentiated from the primitive reptile stock; and the first mammals themselves appeared nearly as early as the first of the dinosaurs.

PELYCOSAURS. A first stage in the differentiation of mammals from other reptile stocks is that of the pelycosaurs, well represented by fossils in the Texas redbeds. These beds date from the late Carboniferous and Lower Permian, a time when the stem reptiles still flourished and ruling reptiles were unheard of. Among the pelycosaurs were all the progressive carnivores of the day. In many features they still had not departed far from the primitive reptile stock. They were a bit more slimly built, but the limbs still sprawled out at the sides in primitive fashion. Some of the more generalized types were rather lizard-like in appearance. Others, such as *Dimetrodon* and *Edaphosaurus*, were remarkably specialized. These odd forms (the former the most common carnivore of the Permian) had long spines growing out from the back, supporting a sail-like flap of skin; what function (if any) this structure served is quite unknown.

THERAPSIDS. In the Karroo beds of South Africa, dating from the later Permian and Triassic, we find that the most common of animals were mammal-like reptiles presumably descended from the pelycosaurs. Close to the main line of evolution of the group and far along towards the mammalian condition was *Cynognathus* ('dog-jaw'). This was, for such an early reptile, a rather lightly built and seemingly active four-footed carnivore, with a maximum length of four or five feet. The skull was intermediate in type between that of a primitive reptile and a mammal; many of the bones absent in mammals were here on their way towards reduction or were already lost. A small third eye was still present on the top of the skull, but its opening was a tiny one. The brain cavity was still small, and the brain still presumably reptilian in type. In the jaw all the original elements were still present, but the dentary was far larger than the other bones. The old single condyle had been replaced by a double one, and in the roof of the mouth a secondary palate had developed, just as in mammals. The teeth, too, were approaching mammalian conditions. There was already a differentiation into incisors, canines, and cheek teeth. In the

A primitive mammal-like reptile, the pelycosaur, *Ophiacodon*, from the late Carboniferous of North America. Some of the members of this group developed peculiar sails along the back and other specializations; *Ophiacodon* is more generalized and represents a very early stage in the differentiation of our ancestors from the primitive reptile stock. (A drawing by L. I. Price, from Raymond, *Prehistoric Life*)

ear there was still but a single auditory bone for sound transmission.

Markedly changed, too, were the limbs. These had already shifted far towards their fore-and-aft mammalian position, and the bones were already much modified to meet the new conditions. In *Cynognathus* and its close allies the count of the toe joints was still that of primitive reptiles, but the joints which were destined to be lost were tiny, and in some other mammal-like forms the number had been reduced to that of mammals.

Cynognathus was thus a very advanced, mammal-like form in

most of its skeletal parts. But what of the other features of soft anatomy which are so important in mammal development? Were these animals already warm blooded? Had they hair or scales? Did they nurse their young? We cannot, of course, give any positive answer to these questions. But the general progress shown in the skeleton suggests similar advances in other respects; the development of a secondary palate, so useful in a warm-blooded animal, appears significant. We arbitrarily group *Cynognathus* as a reptile (we have to draw a line somewhere), but were he alive, he probably would seem to us an odd cross between a lizard and a dog, a transitional type between two great groups of backboned animals.

There were many variants among the mammal-like reptiles in these Karroo beds of South Africa. Some were still not far from the pelycosaur pattern; others were even more mammal-like in some respects than the dog-jawed reptile described above. Many were far off the main line, as, for example, the dicynodonts, or two-tuskers, lumbering plant-eating forms.

These mammal-like forms were the commonest of reptiles during the later Permian and the early Triassic. But during the latter period occurred the development of the ruling reptiles. The archosaurs soon crowded the mammal-like reptiles out, and they disappeared at the end of this, the first period of the Age of Reptiles. They were, however, destined to live on in their mammalian descendants; for the first faint traces of mammals appear in rocks of late Triassic age, and primitive mammals continued to be present throughout the Mesozoic as obscure contemporaries of the great dinosaurs.

EGG-LAYING MAMMALS

A primitive stage in mammal development is that represented to-day by two curious Australian types, the duckbill (*Ornitho-rhynchus*) and the spiny anteater (*Echidna*). These are very highly specialized creatures, leading specialized lives. Both are toothless as adults (the young duckbill has a few tooth rudiments). The duckbill is a good swimmer, being mainly a stream dweller, but also a good digger, nesting in burrows in the banks. The absence of teeth is compensated for by the development of a broad horny bill. The anteater is protected by a stout spiny covering comparable to that of the hedgehog; in relation to its anteating habits there are powerful digging feet and a long slim snout. Both forms are certainly mammals, having fur and nursing their young. But there are many primitive reptilian features; the most conspicuous and important is the fact that they still lay eggs in reptilian fashion!

These animals thus represent the most primitive, the most reptilian, stage in the development of mammals. It is unfortunate that they are so highly specialized in their mode of life, for the egg-laying ancestors of higher mammals were certainly neither duckbills nor anteaters; and the lack of teeth (the most frequently preserved parts in fossil mammals) renders it difficult to compare them with extinct forms. It is probable, however, that most of the mammals of even Mesozoic days had already abandoned egg-laying habits and bore their young alive and that these curious living types have had a separate line of ancestry since the earliest (Triassic) days of mammalian history.

The preservation to modern times of archaic animals of any sort is usually attributable to isolation. An animal may attain isolation geographically, or it may become isolated by taking up a mode of life in which there is little competition. Both factors have operated to save these odd mammals. Their mode of life is extraordinary, in the proper sense of the term; and in Australia they are in a region in which the other mammals also are of a comparatively unprogressive type.

PRIMITIVE MAMMALS OF THE AGE OF REPTILES

With the exception of these egg-laying forms, all existing mammals bear their young alive; the egg is retained inside the mother's body, and thus given additional protection. Bigger, if fewer, offspring seems to have been the mammalian trend – 'quality, not quantity'. It is probable that this stage had been attained by the characteristic mammal groups of the Jurassic and Cretaceous. These Mesozoic mammals, contemporaries of the great dinosaurs, are poorly known. For the length of the Jurassic and Cretaceous, a period estimated at about sixty millions of years, we know of mammals not one whole skeleton, and (until near the close of the Age of Reptiles) not even a complete skull. Our knowledge of these forms is gained almost entirely from teeth and jaws, and even these are quite rare.

Typical Mesozoic mammals were, on the average, no bigger

than a rat or mouse and may have resembled these living forms in general appearance (although not in structure). Their teeth were sharp; they were seemingly flesh-eaters in their tendencies, as had been their reptilian ancestors, but most of them were too small to attack other vertebrates. Probably insects and worms were their main diet, eked out by buds, eggs, and whatever came to hand. Their brains, as far as can be told, were still poor by modern mammalian standards but showed great improvement over those of reptiles. Presumably these forms were very inconspicuous in their habits, dwelling in wooded or bushy regions. There are suggestive features indicating a tree-dwelling life, and, as is the case with many mammals to-day, they may have been nocturnal. Inconspicuous and small they had to remain, for, as contemporaries of the dinosaurs, the threat of death from the great carnivorous reptiles lay constantly over them.

But this long period of 'trial and tribulation' was not altogether disadvantageous. It was, it would seem, a period of training during which mammalian characters were being perfected, wits sharpened. As a result, when, at the close of the Cretaceous, the great reptiles finally died out and the world was left bare for newer types of life, higher mammals prepared to take the leading place in the evolutionary drama had already evolved.

THE AGE OF MAMMALS

In our study of mammals we shall have much to say of the sequence of appearance of various forms. To do this satisfactorily, it is necessary to know something of the geologic time-table of the Cenozoic era, the Age of Mammals. We may regard this era as including two periods, Tertiary and Quaternary, the last short and reaching to modern times. These periods are subdivided to form some seven epochs, which are indicated on the accompanying table. In the older epochs the mammals were mainly of archaic kinds, gradually giving place to the ancestors of the existing types. In the later epochs of the Tertiary there is considerable evidence of a gradual cooling of the North Temperate regions. This cooling culminated in the Pleistocene Ice Age in which portions of Europe and North America were several times covered with great glacial sheets of ice.

Subdivisions of the Cenozoic Era or Age of Mammals		
Periods	Epochs	Estimated Time since Beginning of Epoch in Millions of Years
QUATERNARY	Recent	1/50
	Pleistocene	1
TERTIARY	Pliocene	7
	Miocene	19
	Oligocene	30
	Eocene	45
	Paleocene	55

POUCHED MAMMALS

In the late Cretaceous beds we find that the evolution of mammals during the reign of the dinosaurs had already resulted in the development of the two great living groups of mammals – the marsupials and placentals.

OPOSSUMS. Of these two groups the marsupials, or pouched mammals, are the more primitive and were the more abundant in the last days of the dinosaurs. The living opossum is a typical marsupial and in habits and many structures seems to be very similar to the Mesozoic mammals. The mammal egg contains little yolk, and, when first mammals began to bear their young alive, there was no satisfactory mechanism by which the mother could supply nourishment to the unborn young within her. In consequence, the young were born at a very tiny and immature stage of development. In our own case prematurely born babies are reared in an incubator; the marsupials have evolved a substitute in the pouch, or marsupium, from which the group takes its name. The tiny, seemingly helpless marsupial 'baby' crawls up the mother's body and gains entrance to the pouch on the belly of the mother. Here it finds shelter and warmth; and here, too, are placed the mother's teats from which it gains nourishment to grow to a stage where it is ready to face the world.

There were numerous pouched mammals present in the last days of dinosaur supremacy, animals much like the living opossum in build but mainly of much smaller size. At the dawn of the Age of Mammals the opossums were widespread over the earth. In most regions, however, they made little progress, for they were accompanied by higher mammal types which rapidly supplanted them. In two regions, however, they had better luck.

SOUTH AMERICAN MARSUPIALS. The continent of South America is now connected with the rest of the world by only the narrow Isthmus of Panama. This connexion appears to have been broken at the dawn of the Age of Mammals and did not reform until a very late stage of Cenozoic history. A number of placentals reached that continent and in its isolation developed into many strange and curious herbivorous types considered in later chapters. None of the placental carnivore types such as dogs and cats entered South America before the bars went down. But opossums are omnivorous in their food habits, and some of their descendants developed in South America into flesh-eaters paralleling the wolves and cats of other continents. In the Pleistocene, however, North American connexions became re-established, placental flesh-eaters poured in, and the carnivorous marsupials disappeared, leaving there only the opossums and a few other small pouched mammals.

AUSTRALIAN MARSUPIALS. In Australia the pouched mammals had their one great opportunity. That continent is isolated to-day and seems to have been isolated since the Cretaceous. Pouched mammals had entered Australia before its isolation, but not a single high mammal of any sort, and until man arrived no land mammals had entered since (except, of course, bats and some rats, which seem to have gradually worked their way down the East Indies). There was a whole continent free for the marsupials to (literally) spread themselves in; and there they developed into a curious and interesting fauna, the members of which in many ways have paralleled groups of higher mammals which were evolved in the other continental areas.

The opossum, which seems to lie at the base of the Australian evolutionary array, is an arboreal animal with an omnivorous diet. From such a form we might have – and have had – Australian evolutionary lines leading in both carnivorous and herbivorous directions. Some small Australian marsupials which are still arboreal but have started a carnivorous career are sometimes termed native 'cats'; farther along in this evolutionary line is the Tasmanian devil, a powerful wolverine-like flesh-eater, and the Tasmanian 'wolf', very wolflike in appearance and habits but a good pouched type quite unrelated to the wolves. Side branches of this stock have resulted in the evolution of a specialized anteater comparable to placental forms and a 'mole' which in almost every detail is a duplicate of the golden mole of South Africa, a true placental mammal.

On the other hand, the primitive opossum type has given rise in Australia to many herbivorous forms. The centre stock of these are the phalangers, often called native squirrels. Their habits and appearance are quite squirrel-like, and there are even pouched 'flying squirrels' as an extreme example of parallelism. Other herbivorous forms include the koala, or native 'bear', which does look rather like a Teddy bear, and the wombat, a woodchuck-like animal. A peculiar development is that which has resulted in the kangaroos, ground-dwelling herbivores which have gained speed not by the evolution of hoods (as in the larger herbivorous placentals) but by the taking-up of a hopping gait.

We know little of the fossil history of these living Australian animals except that in the Pleistocene there were a number of larger forms, now extinct, related to the living marsupials of that continent. These included giant kangaroos and giant wombats grown to the size of a rhinoceros.

This interesting Australian development was possible only because of the isolation of these rather primitive mammals; and with the breaking of this isolation by the arrival of man, the Australian fauna seems on the road to extinction. Besides the inroads made by the fur trade, the introduction by man of other animals has done immense harm. Dogs and cats have found the marsupial an easy prey; and the introduction of the rabbit has proved a calamity both to man and to the native animals.

PRIMITIVE PLACENTALS

Beyond the conditions found in the marsupials, there is one final stage in the general line of mammalian ascent which was still necessary to bring them to their highest development – the evolution of primitive placentals.

DEVELOPMENT OF THE PLACENTA. We have noted that a flaw in the process of bearing the young alive lay in the fact that the young, when born, were very tiny and helpless, owing to lack of sufficient means of nourishment before birth. The marsupial pouch has been fairly effective in filling this want. But the other mammals have done a better job. One of the membranes (the allantois) which surrounded the developing egg of the reptile ancestors has in higher mammals come into contact with the walls of the uterus in which the developing embryo lies (cf. p. 389). Through the walls of this fused area, the placenta, food, and oxygen are carried from the mother to the embryo and permit it to grow to a far higher stage before birth than was otherwise possible. With a long period of development before birth and a long period of protection and training after birth, the placental mammal can slowly mature its complicated mechanisms in brain and body. It can, as a result, function more efficiently as an adult than lower forms in which, so to speak, the body has of necessity to be somewhat hastily thrown together.

The higher mammalian groups evolved an efficient placenta at a very early time; presumably much of their success has been due to their development of this useful reproductive mechanism. But they had no 'patent' on this structure; and, while most marsupials have no placenta or a very inefficient one, one Australian genus has finally achieved a placental structure very similar to that of higher mammals. However, this development in marsupials has been too slow to do the group much good; it is too late for the pouched mammals to try to compete with their true placental cousins with which we are concerned from now onwards.

INSECTIVORES. The ancestral placentals were seemingly, like the majority of the small early mammals, rather general in their food habits but primarily insect-eaters. Among the placental mammals there are still a few forms, mainly rather small and inconspicuous, which have retained such feeding habits to this day and seem on the whole to have departed least from the primitive placental stock. The more familiar insectivores are the mole and hedgehog; we have here, as in the case of the egg-laying mammals, an example of the persistence of primitive animals due to an isolated and specialized mode of life.

A more generalized type is that of the shrews – small creatures, mouse-like in appearance. These are not uncommon but are unfamiliar to most of us because of their small size and shy habits – features in which they presumably are similar to their ancient Mesozoic ancestors. The shrews include the smallest of mammals, one species weighing no more than a ten-cent piece. They are extremely nervous little creatures, almost incessantly active. Correlated with this and owing in great measure to the fact that their small size results in a relatively high loss of heat through the skin, shrews eat voraciously to obtain food with which to stoke the furnaces of their bodies. A typical shrew will eat its own weight in food daily.

The oldest placental mammals. These figures represent two of six known skulls pertaining to the ancestors of the advanced mammalian groups. All are from the Cretaceous of Mongolia; the original skulls are but an inch or two in length and represent forms somewhat similar to the shrews of to-day. (From Gregory)

Of especial interest is a modest group of insectivores from the Old World tropics, the tree shrews. Although the trees were probably the ancestral home of placental mammals, most insectivores have turned towards terrestrial or even subterranean modes of life; the tree shrews alone are persistently arboreal. Apart from their retention of this primitive habitat, the tree shrews are important in that they appear to represent the primitive stock from which sprang the primates. Despite the fact that their appearance shows no indication of relationship to monkeys, apes, or men, many points in tree-shrew anatomy show significant primate resemblances.

The oldest of insect-eating placentals have been discovered but recently in Mongolia in the shape of a few tiny skulls of animals contemporary with the late Cretaceous dinosaurs. This final stage in mammal evolution had been reached towards the end of the long Mesozoic 'training period'. When the Age of Reptiles had closed and the dinosaurs had vanished, these efficient placentals were fully prepared to take over the world, and their spread was rapid. During the Paleocene, first of

Tertiary epochs, there was a speedy differentiation from the primitive small insect-eaters into a variety of diverse evolutionary lines and a strong tendency for increase in size. By the Eocene the main lines of mammalian evolutionary history had been established. Few of the original insect-eaters have survived; but all the great array of living higher mammals, from men to whales, from horses to rats, have come from this insectivore stock.

CHAPTER 10

Flesh-Eating Mammals

WE may reasonably begin our discussion of the more highly evolved mammals, the placentals, by giving a brief history of the carnivores, the flesh-eaters. The early mammals were mainly insectivores, forms which presumably ate a bit of this and that but subsisted mainly upon insects and worms. This is flesh-eating of a sort; and it needed only an increase in size before some of the descendants of the insect-eating mammals were capable of preying upon their vertebrate relatives and became carnivorous successors of the flesh-eating therapsids and dinosaurs.

CARNIVOROUS ADAPTATIONS

TEETH. The major changes which have been brought about in mammals of carnivorous habits are concerned with the teeth. The carnivore has to make its kill mainly with its teeth and has to pierce stout hide, cut tough tendons and hard bones. On the other hand, flesh is comparatively simple to digest and need not be well chewed. We find, in relation to this, that in the more strictly flesh-eating forms grinding molar teeth have been reduced almost to the vanishing-point. A cat, for example, has no chewing power whatever. Dogs and their kin, adhering less strictly to a carnivorous diet, have kept all their molars except one upper pair and have retained some grinding surface in their cheek teeth; the bears have veered sharply away from the flesh-eating habits of their ancestors and have re-developed considerable chewing powers.

The front part of the dentition is highly developed. The incisors are highly useful in biting and tearing; the canines, or 'dog-teeth', are long and pointed stabbing weapons in all flesh-eaters. Such cheek teeth as are left generally have sharp ridges and pointed cusps rather than flat surfaces. In all typical carnivores there has developed on either side of the jaw a very specialized pair of teeth called 'carnassials', which function in an important way in cutting hard pieces of food (notice, e.g., how the house cat works a bone around to the side of the mouth to crack it). One of the upper teeth (the last premolar in living forms) and the lower tooth behind it become very large and much elongated, with a sharp fore-and-aft ridge. The two teeth do not meet directly in a straight chopping motion but pass each other, the upper tooth to the outside, acting as a pair of shears which can crack and slice very tough materials.

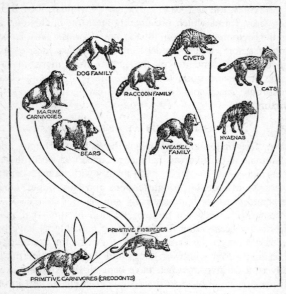

A simplified family tree of the carnivores.

SKELETON. But while the teeth are much modified in carnivores, the skeleton of the trunk and limbs is generally rather primitive in pattern. A carnivore must be speedy to catch its prey. But it cannot develop the rigid skeleton or the hoofed condition with a reduction in toes which we find in the large herbivores discussed in the following chapters. It must remain supple and retain its claws in order to attack and grapple with its prey. There are well-developed claws in all typical carnivores, and, except for a frequent loss of the 'thumb' and big toe, the toes are all retained.

ARCHAIC FLESH-EATERS

Carnivores needed only, for their inception, to have some of their placental cousins develop into harmless herbivorous types upon which they might prey. The development of such herbivores, particularly the archaic ungulates, began promptly with the extinction of the dinosaurs. In the Paleocene, first of the Tertiary periods, there just as promptly began the development of carnivores, to which they fell a prey.

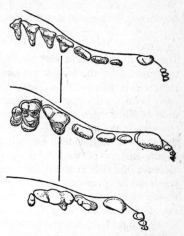

Some of the early carnivores were almost indistinguishable from the ancestral insectivores from which they were being differentiated. But quite rapidly the old carnivores spread out into a number of types with divergent adaptations. The various flesh-eating forms which were dominant in the first two epochs of the Tertiary (the Paleocene and Eocene) are often grouped as archaic carnivores, or creodonts, now entirely extinct. In almost all of them shearing carnassial teeth were developed, although the pair of cheek teeth selected for

Crown view of the upper teeth of the right side in various carnivores. *Above, Sinopa,* a little-specialized Eocene creodont, with all teeth present. *Centre,* a fossil dog; the last molar is lost, the other two molars have some chewing power, and the triangular tooth in front of these (the last premolar) is a specialized shearing tooth (carnassial). *Below,* a cat; shearing is highly developed, but chewing ability is gone; of the molars there remains only a single vestigial tooth. The straight line connects the last premolar, or carnassial, in the three types.

this use varied. The brain was usually small, and presumably the intelligence was nothing to boast of; but this mattered little, for the archaic herbivores which formed the main staple in their diet were equally feeble in brain development. In most of these old carnivores the body was long but the limbs short and the speed consequently slight; but, again, the older hoofed animals were also comparatively slow of gait.

Some of the smaller creodonts seem to have been comparable to modern weasels in their habits; others were more wolf- or lionlike. The range in size was great. Among the large members of the old stock may be mentioned *Hyaenodon* (with stout, hyena-like teeth), which survived until the Oligocene and may have preyed upon the great titanotheres. A contemporary Mongolian carnivore had a skull a yard long; this beast was the largest flesh-eater that land mammals have ever produced.

MODERN TERRESTRIAL CARNIVORES

The end of the Eocene and the beginning of the Oligocene saw the downfall of the archaic creodonts and their replacement by more modern flesh-eaters, the fissipedes, ancestral to the dogs, cats, bears, and other living types. (The name 'split feet' is used to distinguish them from the web-footed sea carnivores.)

SPEED AND BRAINS. If we seek for the cause of this revolution in the flesh-eaters, we naturally turn to an examination of the history of the herbivores forming their food supply. Here we find that at about the beginning of the Oligocene there was a similar overturn of stocks. The archaic ungulates and the more clumsy odd-toed types (such as titanotheres) were passing out of existence and being replaced by speedier, hoofed mammals which would have been able to elude many of the rather slow creodonts which had previously abounded. Then, too, the older ungulates were small-brained forms; their successors seem to have tended towards larger brain development and greater intelligence. This latter feature may perhaps be the real clue to the downfall of the creodonts. It takes brains to stalk a prey; if the would-be eater is more stupid than his potential dinner, his chances are poor. Among all the creodonts there was only one comparatively inconspicuous Eocene group (miacids) in which a good brain was developing; it is from this one stock that all later flesh-eaters have arisen.

AN EARLY FISSIPEDE. Typical of the early members of the modern carnivores which appeared at the end of the Eocene and beginning of the Oligocene was the little *Cynodictis*, about the size of a weasel or a toy fox terrier. This 'dog-weasel' is usually regarded as the ancestor of the later dogs. This may well be correct; but *Cynodictis* was little specialized in any particular direction and may have been close to the starting-point of all the later carnivore lines. The body was long, the limbs rather short, as is still the case with such types as the arboreal weasels or civets. This suggests that the ancestors of modern carnivores had been tree dwellers to start with. In brain size *Cynodictis* was much better off proportionately than any creodont; this increase in intelligence may have been (as we shall see much more markedly in the case of our own ancestors) developed in relation to the complexities of arboreal life.

In the Oligocene the differentiation of the modern carnivore families had already begun. Living, land flesh-eaters are divided by technical characters into two main groups: one including civets, hyenas, cats, and their relatives; the other group the dogs, raccoons, bears, weasels, and their kin.

CIVETS. In the first group the cats are the most familiar forms, but the civet family, including the mongoose, genets, and many other small Old World flesh-eaters, is much closer to the basic stock. These tropical animals have never reached America. They are still arboreal in habits, with the short limbs and small size of their early ancestors; they occupy, roughly, in the tropics the place taken by the weasels and their kin in the North Temperate Zone. Madagascar appears to have been early separated from the continent of Africa, and, of carnivores, it has been populated only by the civet group.

HYENAS. Likewise an exclusively Old World family are the hyenas. These are large and repulsive scavengers, with stout teeth capable of dealing with the leavings of their more delicate carnivorous cousins; they are also not averse to a bit of grave-robbing. They have developed at a comparatively late time from the civets.

CATS. Much older in origin are the felids, the cats, which were already prominent in early Oligocene days. These are the most purely carnivorous of carnivores; behind their carnassials there is scarcely a trace of molar teeth; a cat is ably equipped for stabbing, biting, and slicing; for chewing it is not equipped at all. Rather in contrast to the dogs, which often run their prey down and hunt in packs, the cat is a crafty individualist. The agile body is incapable of sustaining speedy running for long distances; stalking and a sudden jump on the prey is the cat method. The claws are highly developed as a useful aid. Modern cats are of many kinds: the domestic pussy, various wild cats, lion, tiger, and so on. (Beware, by the way, the thrilling jungle picture which shows both lions and tigers. That picture was made in Hollywood, and the animals came from the zoo, for there are no tigers in Africa, and lions are almost extinct in Asia.) These various cats look quite different superficially; but under their skins they are very similar to one another; it is practically impossible, for example, to tell a lion's skull from that of a tiger. Our domestic cat is probably one of the latest additions to man's animal entourage, derived from an African wildcat almost identical in appearance with a striped alley tom.

SABRETOOTHS. Quite sharply marked off from the ordinary members of the cat family were the sabre-toothed cats, now

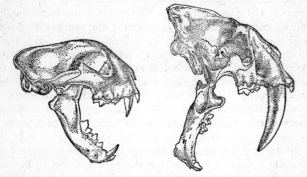

The skull and jaws of a typical cat (*left*) and a sabretooth (*right*). In both the jaws are opened to their full extent. In the sabretooths the whole skull and jaw is shaped to assist in this wide gape and to aid the downward drive of the sabres.

entirely extinct, but formerly widespread. *Smilodon*, a Pleistocene form, was a common inhabitant of the U.S.A. until fairly recent times, geologically speaking. Its skeleton is to be found in every respectable museum, for exceedingly numerous remains have been found at the Rancho la Brea pits in California. At this place in the suburbs of Los Angeles there were, during a late stage of the Pleistocene, pools to which animals of the region came to drink. Beneath the surface were deposits of soft tar. Any unwary animal that stepped in it was trapped. The presence of struggling animals brought, in search of food, numerous flesh-eaters, notably sabretooths and an extinct wolf type and a giant vulture. These forms were very frequently trapped in their turn. In recent decades large quantities of skeletons have been excavated from the now hardened tar.

Smilodon was a powerful animal as large as a tiger. But there were major differences from the ordinary felines. The lower canine teeth were small; the upper ones, on the contrary, were exceedingly long, curved sabres, capable of inflicting a deep slashing wound. The lower jaw was so articulated that it could be dropped at a right angle to clear the sabres; and the shape of the skull indicates the possession of strong muscles to stiffen the head during the stabbing and slicing stroke of the upper canines.

It seems probable that this sabretooth development was an adaptation which fitted these old cats for dealing with thick-skinned animals such as proboscidians. The ordinary carnivore usually tries for a quick kill – a bite into a vital structure. This, however, is almost impossible in an animal with a thick hide. But long slashes of these sabres would make profusely bleeding wounds, followed eventually by death. The sabretooth played a waiting game, it would seem.

The extinction of these animals is very possibly due to the practical extinction of the large thick-skinned animals which may have formed their prey. In the Pleistocene, for example, there were four large and common proboscidians in North America, as well as numerous large ground sloths. To-day all are extinct. It may be that the mastodons – primitive elephant-like forms – were an especial favourite of these creatures, for both *Smilodon* and mastodon survived to the end of the Pleistocene in America, but both disappeared much earlier in Europe.

WEASELS. The second great group of modern land carnivores is that of the dogs, raccoons, bears, weasels, and related types. Among these forms members of the weasel family are closest to the original fissipedes in a number of respects, such as their frequent persistence in an arboreal life and their usual small size and short-legged build. These forms are the north-temperate parallel to the tropical civets. Weasels, martens, and fishers are characteristic of purely carnivorous forms, but there is a considerable amount of variation in the family. The skunks are somewhat less carnivorous in habits and have a rather mixed diet. The wolverine and the badgers are large members of the group. The otter has taken up a fish-eating mode of life in the streams, and the related sea otter has become a good marine type, paralleling the seals in its adaptations.

DOGS. The dogs, wolves, and foxes and their relatives form a second family of this group. They are mainly plains-dwelling, pack-hunting animals, capable of rapid locomotion for long distances. They are considerably less purely carnivorous in their adaptations than the majority of their weasel relatives; they have, for example, retained two of their three upper molars and have a fair degree of chewing ability. The remains of plains animals are comparatively abundant, and hence our history of fossil dogs is relatively full, from the small Oligocene ancestral types down to those of to-day. There have been many side branches developed from the dog stock, such as extinct hyena-like and bearlike forms. There are numerous doglike forms in the tropics. In the North Temperate regions we have, however, only two types of foxes (red and grey) and the wolf, with the addition, in America, of the coyote. The origin of the domestic dog has been in dispute. Some have claimed the jackal as a progenitor, but the wolf appears to be closely related to the ancestor, if not the ancestor itself.

RACCOONS. The raccoons, together with a few relatives, almost all of them American animals, appear to be quite closely related to the dogs and descended from early members of that family. These likeable little animals have persistently kept to the arboreal habitat of their early ancestors. They have in addition departed further from a carnivorous mode of life; one evidence of this is the fact that the shearing teeth can no longer shear; they have been modified into chewing teeth like the molars behind them. The true panda and the giant panda are the two Old World representatives of this group. These are forms of relatively large size which have tended to come down from the trees.

BEARS. A final stage in the trend away from a carnivorous mode of life is seen in the bears, also members of the dog group of carnivores. These forms, which include the largest of living land carnivores, have in general a mixed diet; the polar bear, in a land where there is little to eat except fish, is the only pure carnivore in the family. The last molar tooth had, it would seem, already vanished before the bears drifted back towards a herbivorous type of diet, and teeth, like other structural features generally, when once gone never reappear. But in bears the lack of a full set of back teeth has been made up for by the great elongation of the two molars which are left – the two do the work of three. In the Miocene there were several large and rather heavily built dog types which seem to be intermediate between dogs and bears in structure.

Apart from the polar bear and a few tropical forms, the modern bears belong to two groups – that of the black bears and that including the brown and grizzly bears. In the second category is a large cave bear, which is found as a fossil in Ice Age caves in Europe, and the giant Kadiak bears of Alaska.

AQUATIC CARNIVORES. A final group of carnivores is that of the purely marine types, the pinnipeds, including the various seals and the walrus. These are fish-feeding forms (except for the walrus, a mollusc-eater) which very probably have descended from some primitive dog stock; their fossil history is poorly known. A curious feature is that the tail had seemingly become too feeble a structure in their land ancestors for it to resume a rudder function. The hind legs (reduced in other marine mammals) have remained large and have turned back as a substitute for the missing tail.

The seals come ashore but, for the most part, only at the breeding season. The peculiar structure of the limbs renders them practically helpless and a prey to any large predatory animal, such as man. We are not, technically, carnivores ourselves. But as destroyers of life, not only the lives of other animals, but those of our own kind, we are unquestionably without a peer in the animal kingdom.

CHAPTER 11

Hoofed Mammals

QUITE in contrast to the carnivores just discussed are the hoofed mammals, or ungulates, of which several groups will be considered in the present chapter. By this term may be designated almost all the larger herbivorous mammals. The name, however, is not entirely a distinctive one, for while typical ungulates, such as the horse and cow, have hoofs, the ungulate orders include a number of animals with well-developed claws and even such types as the purely aquatic sea cows. Nor do the ungulates form a single natural group, for the hoofed condition has undoubtedly been attained independently by various lines; and, strange as it may seem, a cow is, for example, probably as closely related to a lion as to a horse.

UNGULATE STRUCTURES

Despite the artificial nature of the ungulate assemblage, there are certain structural changes which have generally happened in the transformation of a primitive mammal of whatsoever group into a large herbivore – changes having chiefly to do with teeth and limbs.

TEETH. The sharp, pointed cheek teeth of primitive mammals were unfitted for a purely vegetable diet and were not suitable organs for undertaking the thorough chewing which leaves, grain, or grass must undergo before passing into the stomach. In relation to this we find that in ungulates the cheek teeth have generally tended to become much enlarged and to develop a flattened grinding surface. In large forms, and especially in animals (as, e.g., horses and cattle) which eat highly abrasive material such as grass, the demands for increased grinding surface on the teeth are very great. In correlation with this the molars of many ungulates become high-crowned, the originally low cusps rising to a great height above the roots but bound together into a solid mass by a covering of cement, a material confined to the roots of the teeth in ordinary mammals.

LIMBS. In most ungulates there is developed a fast type of locomotion. Speed is necessary for these harmless forms if they are to escape flesh-eating enemies, and long-distance transportation is essential for many ungulates which range from season to season over different feeding grounds. In primitive mammals the skeleton was a flexible one; in ungulates the joints of the various bones are so constructed as to be extremely efficient for straightaway forward motion but very poorly adapted for any other types of movement (we all know, for example, how difficult it is for a horse to regain its feet after it has fallen in an unaccustomed position on a slippery pavement). In running types the first joints of the limbs (humerus and femur) are short, giving a fast muscular drive, and the second segments long, swinging fore and aft over a wide angle. In addition, the bones which lie in the palm and sole are much elongated, and by thus running on its toes the animal adds a third functional segment to the limb. With further development of speed the toes themselves are lifted until the animal touches the ground only with their tips. With the result of attaining solid stance, hoofs are developed. A herbivore in general no longer needs claws, and these horny structures become short and broad and surround the end joint of each toe.

With the lifting of the feet into the ungulate position, it is obvious that there will be a tendency for the short side toes to fail to reach the ground and cease to function. In many ungulate groups these side toes are reduced and the central ones strengthened. The 'thumb' and big toe, which were short and primitively diverged from the others, have usually disappeared early in ungulates. Beyond this we find, as we shall see, two different types of toe reduction in hoofed mammals – one in which the axis of the foot lies through the middle toe, leading to the development of three- and one-toed types such as the horses and rhinoceroses; a second in which the axis lies between the third and fourth toes, leading to the development of two-toed, 'cloven-hoofed' types such as the pigs, deer, and cattle.

The type of limb structure just described is that found in most small- or medium-sized ungulates. In large forms, such as elephants, a different series of problems is encountered, and the limb construction for the support of a heavy weight is quite a different one. The limbs are comparatively short, straight, and thick; the thigh is long, the shin short. The foot is broad; there is little tendency to loss of toes; these are short and stumpy and usually have a pad beneath them, forming a stout terminus for the pillar of the limb.

Speed is, of course, the best defence a harmless herbivore has against a carnivore. But, in addition, we find defensive weapons in many ungulate types. Some hoofed mammals, such as the swine or some of the small deerlike forms, have large stabbing canine teeth. Much more common, however, is the development of horn-like structures of one sort or another.

EARLY UNGULATES

CONDYLARTHS. Hoofed mammals are unknown during the Age of Reptiles but made their appearance in considerable numbers even in the Paleocene, earliest of Tertiary epochs. Fairly representative of an early stage in ungulate history is *Phenacodus* of the Lower Eocene of North America and Europe. This animal reached a size rather considerable for the time, the largest species attaining the dimensions of a tapir. In general appearance it resembled some of the early carnivores, for the body and tail were long and the limbs fairly short and primitive in structure. There are, however, good signs that this form was already on the road towards higher ungulate conditions, for not only were the cheek teeth expanded for the chewing of vegetable food, but in the feet, while all the toes were still present, each toe was capped by a small hoof.

This interesting form was once believed by some to be the actual ancestor of many of the later hoofed mammals. This cannot be the case, for it is a bit too late in time (it was a contemporary, e.g., of the early horses) and was also somewhat too large to fit into the early ancestral stages of most later lines. But probably its smaller and more poorly known Paleocene relatives of the order Condylarthra were close to the stem of some of the later great ungulate groups.

UINTATHERES. In many lines of mammalian development we may contrast 'archaic' and 'modernized' types. Thus, among carnivores, we have seen the development of archaic forms, the creodonts, which flourished, rapidly reached in many cases a very large size, and then disappeared quickly when placed in competition with other forms of more progressive structure. So among ungulates we find archaic and progressive forms. Most spectacular among the archaic hoofed mammals were the uintatheres (order Dinocerata). These were characteristic of the Paleocene and Eocene. By the end of the latter period some of them reached the size of an elephant. These heavy types were not built for speed; the limbs were powerful, elephant-like columns; all the toes were retained to brace a presumably padded foot. It is probable that the uintatheres were swamp dwellers; but even so they needed protection against the larger contemporary flesh-eaters. Large upper canine tusks were developed as weapons at an early date, and in addition three pairs of hornlike structures projected from the top of the head. Uintatheres were exceedingly small-brained types, and their tooth construction also was too poor to stand anything but the softest of food. With the end of the Eocene this line became extinct.

ODD-TOED UNGULATES

In the Eocene more progressive ungulates were already well started on their careers. Most prominent of ungulates from the Eocene on were two groups – the perissodactyls, or odd-toed

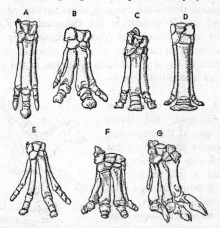

The right front feet of various odd-toed ungulates. *A*, an Oligocene-running rhinoceros; *B*, a four-toed Oligocene true rhinoceros; *C*, a later (Miocene) three-toed rhinoceros; *D*, the gigantic rhinoceros *Baluchitherium*, with a pillar-like foot; *E*, a tapir; *F*, a titanothere; *G*, the chalicothere, *Moropus*. The 'thumb' is absent in all. In some the 'little finger' is present (*B, E, F, G*) but tends to be small and is lost in most rhinoceroses (*A, C, D*). This results in a three-toed condition, as in many of the (related) horses ungulates, and the artiodactyls, the cloven-hoofed or even-toed types; these will be treated in turn.

TOE REDUCTION IN ODD-TOED FORMS. The perissodactyls include, among living hoofed mammals, the horses and their zebra and ass relatives, the rhinoceroses, and the tapirs. In addition there were two interesting extinct families, the titanotheres and chalicotheres. Characteristic of this group is a type of foot symmetry with the axis through the middle toe and a tendency to reduce the toes from five to four or three and, finally, in horses, to one. In order to see how this type of toe reduction has worked out, try the experiment of placing your hand on a table in the flat position of the primitive mammal. Raise the wrist up off the table and the hand is in the position of a primitive hoofed mammal walking on its toes. As this is done, it is obvious that the thumb soon ceases to touch. If this were lost, your hand would be in the four-fingered condition seen in the front foot of the dawn horses or the living tapir. Raise the hand a bit more, and the little finger ceases to touch. An analogous three-toed stage is characteristic of most fossil horses and is still present in the rhinoceroses. And, finally, getting the hand straight up from the table, only the middle finger touches. You have thus in a brief space of time repeated the essentials of the story of limb evolution in the horses from five toes to a one-toed condition.

HORSES. The oldest of horses, *Eohippus*, the dawn horse, appears at the beginning of the Eocene epoch; frequent remains of this tiny horse, no larger than a fox terrier, are found in deposits of that date in the western U.S.A. This form was already a slimly built little fellow with quite long legs; but while toe reduction had already begun, there were still four toes in front and three behind. The cheek teeth of the dawn horse were still

Eohippus and '*Eohomo*', the 'dawn horse', and the 'dawn man', a fanciful sketch made by T. H. Huxley on seeing the remains of the oldest horse. Needless to say the two were not contemporaries – by 50,000,000 years or so. (From Schuchert and Le Vene)

low-crowned and incapable of coping with much hard food; presumably he dwelt in the forests, existing as a browser rather than as a grazing type. *Eohippus* seems surely the beginning of the horse line, but is probably close to the stock from which have come the other odd-toed ungulates as well.

Mesohippus, a typical Oligocene horse, was bigger, the size of a collie or larger. The 'little finger' had been lost, resulting in a count of three toes on all the feet. By the Miocene the main line of horse evolution, leading to such forms as *Parahippus* and *Merychippus*, was acquiring high-crowned teeth, suggesting a grass diet and a change to plains life. This is also borne out by the feet, in which the two side toes, although still present, were becoming slim and short and probably did not normally touch the ground. A single toe is not well adapted to rough going but is an excellent structure on the hard surface of the plains.

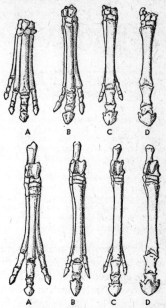

The evolution of the feet in horses. All of the right side; front feet *above*, hind feet *below*. The 'thumb' has disappeared in even the earliest known horses. *A, Eohippus,* a primitive Eocene form with four toes in front and three behind; *B, Miohippus,* an Oligocene three-toed horse; *C, Merychippus,* a late Miocene form with reduced lateral toes; *D, Equus* of the Pleistocene and Recent. (*A* after Cope, *B, C,* after Osborn)

Hipparion and other forms which survived into the Pliocene were the size of a pony and lightly built, fast-running types. Horses had been quite rare in the Old World to begin with, but by the Pliocene, *Hipparion* was widespread over the Northern Hemisphere. During the Pliocene period the side toes tended to disappear, and by the beginning of the Ice Age horses of modern type, with but one complete toe, were present on every continent except Australia.

In the Old World there developed not only true horses but

Crown view of the upper cheek teeth (molars and premolars) of *A*, *Eohippus*; *B*, the modern horse, genus *Equus*. These are of the right side; with the front of the mouth to the right. The simple six-cusped teeth of *Eohippus* have elongated and evolved into a very complicated pattern in the recent forms. The three teeth to the left are the molars. These were already fairly well developed in the early horses. In modern horses three of the more anterior teeth (premolars or 'bicuspids') have gained a form similar to that of the molars.

the closely related zebras and asses. To-day the wild progenitors of the domestic horses are represented by only a rare, shaggy-maned, pony-like form (Prezwalski's horse) from the steppes of Central Asia. Horses were hunted as food by our Stone Age ancestors, but the oldest records of domesticated forms cannot be traced beyond the third millennium before Christ.

America was the cradle of the horse family, and native horses were present there throughout the Pleistocene Ice Age. Subsequent to the last retreat of the ice, however, they became entirely extinct there. The horses are only one of a number of large animals which lived in America at, geologically, a recent period and have since vanished from the continent. Besides horses, ground sloths, glyptodonts, giant armadillos, camels, mastodons, and mammoths all inhabited the United States not so many

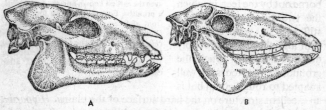

The skulls of *A*, *Eohippus*; *B*, *Equus*, a modern type of horse. In the course of horse evolution, with the lengthening of the tooth row and the development of high-crowned teeth, the face has become very much elongated proportionately and the jaws much deepened to accommodate the teeth.

thousands of years ago. What caused this mass extinction of large American animals (while not touching the smaller forms) we do not know.

TAPIRS. A much less prominent group of odd-toed ungulates

is that of the tapirs. To-day their only living representatives are confined to the tropics of South America and the Malay region. In the Tertiary they inhabited North America and Europe; the cold of the Pleistocene appears to have been responsible for their extermination in these northern latitudes. The tapirs, except for their somewhat larger size and stockier build and the development of a pendant snout, are in many respects quite close to the ancestral horse types. Like the earliest horses, the living tapirs have four toes in the front feet and three behind; like them, the teeth are low-crowned; and the tapirs to-day are persistently forest dwellers. These forms have departed least of all the odd-toed ungulates from the primitive stock of the order.

RHINOCEROSES. The rhinoceroses of the Old World tropics are the living remnants of a once-important group of odd-toed hoofed mammals. They are large, ungainly, three-toed creatures with one or two horns on the top of their long low skulls. These horns are of a peculiar structure. They consist not of true horn or bone but of a bundle of hairs 'glued' together into a compact mass.

Far different were the earliest rhinoceroses which appeared in the Eocene as contemporaries of the early horses. These were comparatively small and slim 'running rhinoceroses', seemingly much like their horse relatives in build, hornless, and at first with four toes still present on the front feet. In the following period there had evolved somewhat more normal three-toed rhinoceroses of larger size and heavier build. Horns, however, were slow to make their appearance and were absent in many early types.

Baluchitherium, an Oligocene hornless form recently excavated in Central Asia, was perhaps the most remarkable of all rhinoceroses. This animal was some seventeen feet in height and was proportioned like a heavily built giraffe. It appears to have been the largest of all terrestrial mammals but was, of course, considerably smaller than some of the dinosaurs.

There were many variants among the older rhinoceroses; short-legged, water-living forms, for example, and the woolly rhinoceros of the Ice Age in Europe, whose warm shaggy pelt is made known to us not only by the drawings of cavemen but also through the fact that two of these forms have been found 'pickled' entire in a Galician oil seep. Rhinoceroses were present in North America as well as in the Old World until the end of the Tertiary. To-day they seem to be a dying group, close to extinction.

TITANOTHERES. An interesting fossil group of odd-toed forms is that of the titanotheres, 'titanic mammals'. These began in the Eocene with forms of somewhat horselike appearance. But there was a rapid tendency towards extremely large size and a ponderous elephantine build (four and three toes were retained on the front and hind limbs, respectively, of these forms to the end of their history). Slow of speed, these big herbivores seem to have been a source of prey for the larger carnivores of their day, and in relation to their needs for defence we find that in a number of distinct types of titanotheres paired bony horns appeared over the nasal region. These forms were almost entirely confined to North America. At the beginning of the Oligocene, giant titanotheres were the commonest of mammals in the western part of the U.S.A., and fossil remains of them are very abundant in the South Dakota Bad Lands. But, following this climax in development of size and numbers of the group, they disappeared abruptly from the fossil record. A possible reason for extinction is the fact that the teeth of these forms were suitable only for the softest of plant food; a slight change in vegetation might have been enough to cause their undoing.

CHALICOTHERES. A final group of odd-toed ungulates is that of the chalicotheres, now quite extinct also but not uncommon during the Tertiary. In general structure these forms were not dissimilar to the horses, while their teeth were quite like those of titanotheres. On both counts we must place them in the group of odd-toed hoofed mammals. But their feet are of such a character as to belie the name, for the toes terminated not in hoofs but in huge claws. So unexpected is such a feature in an ungulate group that it was long argued that we could not include them among the odd-toed forms. But belong here they do. Seemingly, the claws were an adaptation for digging out roots and tubers which may have formed a major part of their diet.

All in all, the odd-toed ungulates have not proved a success. In the early days of mammalian history they were numerous and widespread. But to-day two of the five groups are entirely extinct, and the tapirs and rhinoceroses are greatly reduced in numbers. The horse family has held its own; but even here wild forms are none too common, and the advance of machinery is making inroads on the numbers of our useful domestic horse.

EVEN-TOED UNGULATES

Much more successful, in modern times, have been the even-toed ungulates or artiodactyls. These forms were not as common

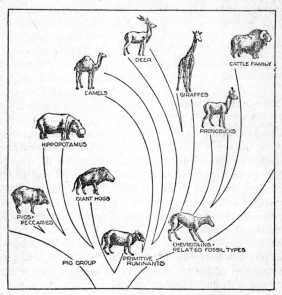

A family tree of the even-toed ungulates (artiodactyls). The major cleavage is into the pig group (*left*) and the cud-chewers, or ruminants (*right*). Among the latter the camels appear to have diverged at an early date.

as their odd-toed rivals in the earliest days of ungulate development, but they have become increasingly prominent during the course of the Age of Mammals and seem to be at the peak of their development at the present time. To this group belong the common large food animals and a host of wild types – pigs and peccaries, the hippopotami, camels, deer, giraffes, cattle, sheep, goats, and antelopes.

TOE REDUCTION IN EVEN-TOED FORMS. To gain an idea of the type of toe reduction encountered in the even-toed forms,

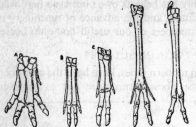

The right front feet of various even-toed ungulates. *A*, an oreodon; *B*, a primitive ruminant; *C*, a peccary; *D*, a primitive deer; *E*, a camel. The 'thumb' was rapidly lost, and the foot tended to become four toed, with toes 2 and 3 more prominent. The lateral toes become reduced to 'dew claws' or disappear, leaving the two centre toes as a 'cloven hoof'. The two bones supporting these toes (metapodials) fuse in most cud-chewers to form a cannon bone.

try again the 'experiment' of hand-lifting mentioned previously for odd-toed types. After the thumb has lifted, the hand is in a four-toed stage, as was the case in many early members of the present group and is still characteristic of the pigs and certain other living forms. If, with four fingers touching, these be shifted about until they rest comfortably on the table, it will be found that the two central ones (third and fourth) project somewhat in advance of the others, and, if the hand is lifted farther, these two alone touch, and the second and fifth are raised from the table. It is this type of toe reduction that has taken place in the higher even-toed forms; the cloven hoof of the sheep or cow in reality consists of two closely applied toes, the third and fourth.

The first even-toed types appeared in the early Eocene, but it was not until the close of that epoch that they became prominent members of animal society. From the first there seems to have been a distinct cleavage into two groups, the swine and their relatives on the one hand, and the cud-chewers, or ruminants, on the other.

PIGLIKE ARTIODACTYLS. The pigs and their relatives are the most primitive of living even-toed forms in many ways. They are still four-toed animals (although the side toes are much reduced), and the limbs are little elongated; not much speed has developed. The diet of the pig is still of a rather primitive, omnivorous type, in contrast to their more advanced ruminant relatives; swine will eat anything from potatoes to rattlesnakes. The pigs and their closest fossil relatives are confined to the Old World. There are found, in addition to the wild boar type from which our domestic porkers are derived, a number of distinct

living forms, including among
others the wart hogs of
Africa and the babirussa of
the East Indies. The pigs
have large canine tusks; these
usually curl outwards and
even upwards at the side of
the skull. In the babirussa
they actually turn straight up
and pierce through the top of
the nose as a peculiar type of

The skull of an Oligocene giant pig
(*Archaeotherium*). The use (if any) of the
bony knobs on the jaw and below the eye
socket is unknown. This skull was about
1¼ feet long; some were about twice this
size. (After Scott)

horn. This might be considered as a useful adaptation if the tusks
stopped there, but they do not. They continue growing and curve
back in a spiral in front of the eyes. Such a seemingly useless
end product of a seemingly useful development constitutes one
of the many puzzles with which the student of evolutionary
processes must deal.

Closely related to the pigs are the peccaries, small and more
lightly built forms in which (as a distinguishing feature) the tusks
grow straight downward in normal fashion. To-day the peccaries
are mainly found in South America, although one type ranges
as far north as Texas. Peccaries passed their early history in
North America, and even during the Ice Age they were numerous
as far north as Michigan and Maryland.

A distant ally of the swine is the hippopotamus, a large water-
living, piglike type now found only in tropical Africa but in the
Pleistocene in regions as far removed as England and China.

In addition there are several extinct groups of animals which
are allied to the swine. Most prominent of these fossil forms
were the 'giant hogs' (entelodonts) of the Oligocene and
Miocene. These were animals of large size, one form being
about as large as a buffalo. The giant hogs were rather more
progressive than their porcine relatives in their limbs, which
were fairly long and in which the toes had been reduced to two.
Peculiar flanges of bone grew down from the sides of the skull
and jaws, suggesting a repulsive appearance; that their dis-
positions were none too good is suggested by the fact that some
fossil skulls show wounds apparently inflicted by the animal's
own kind.

PRIMITIVE RUMINANTS. The piglike forms described above

constitute one division of the even-toed ungulates; the other, and much more important, division of the group is that of the ruminants, or cud-chewers. These forms are, in contrast to the swine, pure vegetarians. In all the living members of this group there is a complicated stomach; partly digested food is returned to the mouth, the 'cud' chewed, and then returned to another stomach compartment to continue its digestive travels. The side toes have tended to disappear fairly rapidly, and living members of the group have but two functional digits, although the lateral ones may be represented by vestigial 'dew claws'. In the earlier periods of the Tertiary there was a great abundance of primitive ruminants, ancestral as a group to later forms but most of them representing side branches of the ruminant stock. Fairly characteristic of these early forms were the oreodonts, which, judging by the abundance of their remains in the White River Bad Lands of South Dakota, must have swarmed the western plains in enormous numbers in Oligocene times. The oreodonts are often called, for want of a better name, 'ruminating swine'. This refers to the fact that, as judged by their teeth, they were closely related to cud-chewing types of to-day and that, on the other hand, the limbs were short and stocky and the general proportions quite piglike. There were four short toes, and in one type even the thumb had been retained.

CAMELS. Even while the oreodonts and other primitive cud-chewers flourished, higher ruminant groups were emerging. The earliest group to develop, and the one most distinct from other ruminants, is that of the camels and llamas. The camels, as we know them to-day, are Old World desert dwellers of large size, with a hump (or two) as a reserve food supply on their backs. There are but two divergent toes on the long limbs, bearing a pad beneath them for better support on soft sands. The llamas and related South American forms are quite different in appearance; they are much smaller mountain and plains dwellers, lacking a hump and covered with a thick coat of wool. These two kinds of animals, however, are closely related despite the differences in looks and their widely separated habitats.

The clue to their distribution lies in the fact that North America was their original home. The little early camels of the Oligocene and Miocene were remarkable for the rapidity with which the side toes were lost and the limbs lengthened.

Presumably the hump is a very recent acquirement in camels; the older members of the family appear to have been plains and glade dwellers rather than desert types. Among the Tertiary camels of North America were a number of distinct types, one small form having the slender build of a gazelle, others developing not only long legs but a long neck similar to that of giraffes.

By Pleistocene times the llamas had gained their present home in South America, and true camels had migrated to Asia. Camels, however, persisted in the Southwest of the U.S.A. until comparatively late times. Why they became extinct is, as in the case of the horses, a mystery, for camels were found to be well adapted to the south-western deserts when reintroduced there by man.

The skull of a fossil ruminant (*Synthetoceras*) from the Pliocene of America. Descended from the primitive musk-deer stock, this form has acquired 'horns', as have other advanced types, but has developed most prominently a huge fused pair above the nostrils. (After Stirton)

CHEVROTAINS AND THEIR FOSSIL RELATIVES.

In contrast to the camels in such features as a still more complicated stomach are the remaining numerous artiodactyl families of which the deer, giraffe, and cattle are representative types. Very primitive members of this group are the chevrotains, or water deer, of south-eastern Asia and tropical Africa. These are tiny animals not much bigger than a large rat in one case and much like miniature deer in appearance. There are no horns of any sort, but there are sharp canine tusks as defensive weapons. They have in some cases four complete toes, a feature retained to-day in none of the other higher ruminants.

These water deer are living relics of a group which flourished greatly during Oligocene times. Some of these older forms were very similar to the chevrotains in size and structure. Others were beginning to branch off into various lines of specialization. Certain of these branches are extinct; others have led to the existing families of higher ruminants described below. In most cases there was a tendency towards increase in size; and while a number of early forms had canines as defensive weapons, most of the advanced types tended to develop horns of some sort or other. Of the extinct groups we may mention as an example one in which several pairs of horns started to develop along the length of the head and in which the dominant pair came to be, in *Synthetoceras*, over the nostrils rather than in the more usual position on the forehead.

DEER. The deer and related forms – elk, moose, reindeer, and so on – have been a comparatively conservative group as far as habits are concerned, for (with low-crowned teeth) they have mainly remained browsers and have rarely left the forests, which appear to have been the original home of the higher artiodactyls. They are essentially animals of the Temperate Zone; very few have entered the tropics, but, on the other hand, they have extended their range into the tundras and barren lands of the Far North.

A most obvious feature of deer structure is the development of antlers. We sometimes speak of a deer's horns; but, properly speaking, a horn should be covered, as is a cow's, with actual horn – a hardened skin material identical in nature with our fingernails. In the case of the deer there is no such structure; the antler consists of bone alone. During the antler's growth it is covered by soft, furry skin – velvet – but this dies and is rubbed off when growth is completed. Antlers differ from horns in two other features. A true horn is a single structure, although it may be variously twisted or coiled, whereas in many deer the antlers are divided into a considerable number of branches, or tines. A still greater difference is the fact that horns are permanent structures, but antlers are shed. Every year the antler breaks off at the base, or burr, and then grows anew to larger size and greater complexity. This seems a very wasteful feature when we think, for example, of the great amount of food which must have gone yearly to build up the gigantic antlers of the great extinct 'Irish elk'.

GIRAFFES. The giraffe is a representative of a further group of higher ruminants. This beast, too, is a browsing form; but the giraffe is a dweller in the savannas rather than the woods and, with limited amounts of trees to graze upon, has evolved a mechanism for getting the most for his money. The long front legs and exceedingly long neck enable it to reach high branches inaccessible to ordinary animals. We have said that higher ruminants all have tended to develop horns of some sort, and the giraffe is no exception, for he bears small, skin-covered bony prongs on the top of his skull.

The giraffe's long neck is an interesting development; but it has not involved the addition of a single bone to the animal's skeleton. The neck of an ordinary mammal contains seven vertebrae; that of the giraffe contains exactly the same number, each one, of course, greatly elongated. On the other hand, we may note that in the whale, in which there is practically no neck and the head is buttressed right in front of the shoulders, there are again just seven neck vertebrae, but each one is exceedingly short. Reptiles, as we have seen, have a great degree of variation in their neck skeletons; mammals, for some unknown reason, almost never depart from the primitive number of neck vertebrae.

Fossil relatives of the giraffes, similar to the living form in most respects, but with short necks, have long been known from Pliocene deposits. It was therefore of considerable interest when there was discovered early in the present century in the forests of the Belgian Congo the okapi, a living, short-necked giraffe relative.

THE PRONGBUCK. The giraffes are entirely Old World types; the one higher ruminant peculiar to North America is the prongbuck of the western plains. This creature has much of the build and habits of the antelopes of the Old World but is quite a distinct type, as is shown by its 'horns'.

These structures consist of a bony core which is never shed and is covered with horn. In these respects the prongbuck agrees with the cattle tribe. But, on the other hand, the prongbuck does shed the horny covering of the horn, and the horn is forked. These characters suggest the deer. To which group does the prongbuck, then, belong? To neither, really; it is a native product, end form of an independent, purely American line of ruminant development of which there are many fossil representatives.

CATTLE AND RELATED TYPES. A final and the largest group of higher ruminants is that of the bovids, including the cattle and their numerous relatives – antelopes, sheep, goats, and other familiar forms. These are mainly plains dwellers, with high-crowned teeth capable, as is the case with horses, of utilizing grass as a food supply. In almost all members of the group true horns have developed, simple although often much-curved structures with a permanent bony core at the centre and tipped with hollow horn. Bovids were comparatively late in their development, for there were but few of them in the Miocene, and it is only towards the end of the Tertiary that they became numerous. But once started on their careers they have swept all before them and are now, in open country of all sorts, the dominant hoofed mammals – indeed, almost the only ones. The oldest forms were not dissimilar to some of the smaller antelopes, active plains dwellers with horns that are often small and comparatively straight. Antelope types are most prevalent in Africa; that region is to-day the centre of artiodactyl evolution.

One familiar side branch of the family is that of the sheep and goats – antelope descendants which have taken to mountain regions and, incidentally, have tended to develop heavy and highly coiled horns. These forms are represented in the highlands of Europe and Asia by numerous wild species, from certain of which have been derived our domestic races.

A second group, which has tended to migrate to colder climates, is that of the muskoxen, which are now confined to the Far North, but which were inhabitants of much more southern regions in Europe and America during the Ice Age just behind us.

Certain of the African antelopes of to-day, such as the harte-beest and the gnu (of crossword-puzzle fame), are quite large and heavily built and with S-shaped horns which are turned out from the side of the head before curving up and forward. These seem to represent the ancestors of the important cattle tribe which appears shortly before the beginning of the Ice Age. Cattle such as the forms from which our domestic races have been derived seem to have ranged widely over the Old World during the days of our old Stone Age ancestors; there was also a giant ox perhaps half again as large as the living forms. This last was still present and hunted in Germany in the Middle Ages, and some of its blood may still flow in a few European herds. Besides the ordinary domestic cattle, there are a number of other related types, such as the water buffaloes in the tropical regions of southern Asia; several of these have also been brought into domestic use. Also closely affiliated to the cattle are the bisons of both Europe and America, now nearly extinct, but common in Pleistocene times.

The history of the cattle-antelope group has been almost entirely confined to the Old World. It was there that these animals had their origin, and it is there that almost all the living wild forms are found to-day. Only three members of the family have successfully invaded North America – the bison and the mountain sheep and mountain 'goat' of the Rockies. This lack of representation is seemingly due to the fact that the family developed late in the Age of Mammals. They were, for the most part, tropical plains dwellers, and only forms such as those above, which can stand cold climates or inhabit mountains, were able to make the (by then) difficult passage from Asia via Alaska.

The even-toed ungulates are, in contrast to the perissodactyls, a flourishing group. To what has their success been due? Perhaps not so much to their good teeth, although they are good, or to good brains – we are the animals that boast of that feature – or, perhaps, to good feet, although there are some clever mechanical adaptations in the limbs of this group; perhaps (since it is the higher ruminants that compose the greater part of the modern artiodactyl population) the development of the stomach may have been the real cause of artiodactyl success.

Which are more important – brains or stomachs? Sometimes, when indigestion hits us, we may think of a good stomach as the really essential thing in life. But, when we sit down to a meal of beef or lamb or pork, we may reflect that brains do seem, on the whole, to have won.

CHAPTER 12

More Ungulates

WHILE the odd- and even-toed groups are the most important of ungulate stocks, they are but two of a dozen or more orders, living and extinct, which are grouped as hoofed mammals. In the present chapter we shall consider two series of ungulates: first, the subungulates, including conies, elephants, and sea cows, and then a varied assemblage of forms, now extinct, which once inhabited South America.

SUBUNGULATES

Under the heading of subungulates are included the conies – small rodent-like creatures from Africa and Syria – the proboscidians, including the elephants and their extinct relatives, the sea cows, and several apparently allied fossil forms. These make up a very diverse assemblage, a seemingly incongruous jumble of land and sea forms, large and small types; but early representatives of the varied groups show fundamental similarities which strongly suggest a common origin; and the fact that the earliest fossil forms are found in Africa suggests that that continent was their common ancestral home.

CONIES. Most primitive of subungulates in many respects are the conies, or dassies (*Hyrax*, etc.), of Africa and southwestern Asia. The word 'coney' was an old English term for 'rabbit' (Coney Island, e.g., means Rabbit Island) but has been used in the English Bible as the best equivalent for the animals now under discussion. The comparison is not inappropriate, for the dassies have chisel-like front teeth and gnawing habits similar to those of the rodents. The comparison would be better, however, with the woodchuck rather than the rabbit as regards general appearance and habits. Most conies are ground dwellers in rocky country, but one type is somewhat arboreal.

But the rodent resemblances are superficial only. The cheek teeth are rather more like those of a miniature rhinoceros than anything else, and the general build of these odd mammals is quite different from that of any common group; they have obviously had a long independent history. This conclusion is borne out by the fossil record. The oldest African land animals of the Age of Mammals are found in the Fayum region of Egypt, in beds of late Eocene and early Oligocene age. In these beds conies are already numerous and varied, one form being as large as a lion. They have never been discovered as fossils outside of Africa and the eastern Mediterranean region and apparently are a group characteristically African in origin.

ELEPHANTS. The elephants are the only living representatives of the proboscidians, mammals with a trunk. These ponderous fellows are the largest living land creatures; of living animals only a few of the whales are larger, and in the past they have been exceeded in bulk only by some of the dinosaurs and one giant rhinoceros. Their great weight has resulted (as in all heavy land animals) in a pillow-like construction of the limbs, the straight legs ending in a broad, padded foot. The skull is very short and high. Of the originally numerous front teeth there remain but two upper incisors which extend forward as the two long curved tusks; above, the nose is extended to form the long flexible proboscis. The cheek teeth are of a very curious nature. All the molars of an ordinary primitive mammal are present, and each one is a very large high-crowned structure with numerous cross-ridges which can undergo considerable wear. The jaw, however, is very short, and the elephants have evolved an odd type of tooth replacement whereby only four of the dozen molars are in place at once, one in each half of each jaw. The teeth are formed one after another in the back part of the jaws and gradually swing around into position as the preceding tooth is ground down to the roots and discarded.

There are but two types of living elephants: the Indian form, which has been domesticated, and the untamed and more primitive African type, readily distinguishable by its very large ears. In the Pleistocene epoch just behind us, however, elephants inhabited all the northern continents and were present in great variety and abundance; to these extinct elephants the term 'mammoth' is usually applied.

Best known of these extinct forms is the northern woolly mammoth, a dweller in cold climates in both Eurasia and North America. Fossil remains of these forms are numerous, and in Siberia many woolly mammoths have been found preserved in natural cold storage, embedded in the frozen tundra. So common

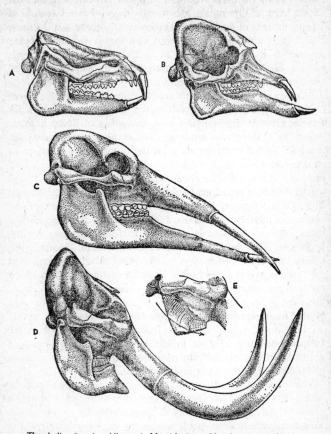

The skulls of proboscidians. *A, Moeritherium,* oldest known member of the group, from the Upper Eocene and Lower Oligocene of Egypt. The skull is fairly normally built; the upper and lower tusks are simple, somewhat elongated incisor teeth. *B, Phiomia,* an Oligocene mastodon with small upper and lower tusks; the jaws are elongated. *C, Trilophodon,* a Miocene long-jawed, four-tusked mastodon. In later mammoths and elephants, as the woolly mammoth (*D*), the lower jaw shortens and the lower tusks disappear. *E,* part of the side of the upper jaw of an elephant. The bone over the teeth is removed to show how the teeth swing down into place as earlier ones are ground down and used up. (*A, B* after Andrews)

are mammoth finds in Siberia that there is a flourishing local trade in fossil ivory, and specimens have been excavated with hair and flesh still present; some years ago guests at a scientific banquet in Russia were served with portions (very small) of mammoth steak!

In both old and new worlds there were extinct mammoths of other types inhabiting temperate and tropical regions. These creatures, to judge by their remains, were quite common, and most are known to have lived beyond the time of recession of the Pleistocene ice sheets. Why they suddenly disappeared over most of their former range is as great a problem as that connected with the extinction in America of horses, camels, and other forms.

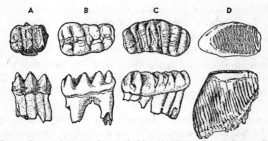

Teeth of mastodons (*A, B*), a primitive elephant (*C*), and the woolly mammoth (*D*), all much reduced. Crown views *above*, side views *below*. The typical mastodon tooth has but a few crests and is low-crowned; the elephant tooth is high-crowned, with numerous closely crowded transverse ridges.

THE OLDEST PROBOSCIDIANS. The elephants are but a final stage in a long history of proboscidian evolution. The most primitive ancestor of the group is found in the same Fayum beds that contain the oldest remains of the conies. *Moeritherium* was no bigger than a good-sized hog and showed few elephantine characters. There was apparently no trunk, although there might have been a piglike type of snout; all the front teeth were present, although one upper and one lower pair were considerably larger than their neighbours; all the grinders were present in normal fashion and were quite simple in construction. In fact, so primitive was this beast, that it has been debated whether it really belongs to the elephant group. A careful analysis shows that a majority of its characteristics are in agreement with those of proboscidians, but it also had many features of the sea cows and some of the conies. *Moeritherium* was apparently close to the common stem from which all three of these diverse groups have sprung.

MASTODONS. In the upper levels of these same Egyptian fossil beds are more progressive proboscidians, the earliest of the mastodons, which flourished from Oligocene to Pleistocene times. In these forms there were, to begin with, two pairs of long incisor teeth which gradually lengthened into tusks. All the older mastodons had tusks in the lower as well as the upper jaws. These tusks were at first straight, at the end of long bony jaws, and with a long nose tube which was probably flexible only at its tip.

Gradually, however, the jaws shortened, the lower tusks were reduced, the upper ones became free at their bases and much curved, and the trunk became the highly flexible structure it is to-day; these features led to the head structure seen in the last of the mastodons and in the elephants. The elephants alone of animals other than man have a chin; but the elephant chin is not (as is ours) a new structure but merely the stump of the jaw which once bore the lower tusks.

The grinding teeth of the early mastodons were of simple construction – low-crowned, with a few cross-ridges, and all in place at the same time. But with increase in size or a trend towards grass rather than softer vegetation as a food supply, we find that the teeth (particularly in the line leading to the elephants) became higher-crowned, increased the number of cross-ridges, and gradually tended towards the peculiar elephant type of tooth succession.

Although mastodons originated in Africa, they spread rapidly over the earth and in the Miocene and Pliocene were found all over the northern land masses and in the Pleistocene even reached South America. In the Old World they seem to have died out near the beginning of the Pleistocene; but in America they survived until within ten or twenty thousand years of modern times.

SIRENIANS. The sea cows of to-day include the dugong of the Indian Ocean and the Red Sea and the manatee of the shores of the tropical Atlantic; a third form (Stellar's sea cow) was formerly present in the region of Bering Strait but was killed off by man. These grotesque mammals are purely aquatic creatures which browse upon the vegetation of coastal waters but never come ashore; the hind legs are lost, the front ones have become steering flippers, and there is a well-developed transverse tail flap. The name of the group recalls the alluring sirens of Greek legend. Even to-day in Aden one is invited in to see (at a price) a mermaid; but one should be forewarned, or the shock of seeing a rather ugly sea cow instead of a beauteous damsel may be too much.

These curious marine mammals with a herbivorous diet are no relation to the whales (which are of flesh-eating origin), nor is there any reptilian parallel to them, except for the seaweed-eating lizards of the Galápagos. Now restricted, they were widespread in Tertiary seas. Most of the oldest sea-cow remains come from Egypt, and these forms show many features suggesting a common ancestry with the conies and elephants. It seems absurd to include these marine and almost limbless animals in a group of 'hoofed' mammals, but the resemblances in the older types are unmistakable.

Our fossil record in Africa is very incomplete, but as far as it goes it suggests that in the earliest part of the Age of Mammals that continent was for millions of years separated from the rest of the world. During that time there developed a peculiar native stock of archaic herbivorous animals which gradually diversified into the conies (as the least specialized representatives), the great proboscidians, and the ancestral sea cows. When, at about the end of the Eocene, interconnexions with Asia were established and other animal types could enter Africa, the conies merely held their own, but the proboscidians migrated outward in triumph. The sea cows, too, migrated but, already far along in aquatic adaptation, radiated outward along marine rather than terrestrial routes. The main evolutionary centre for the mammals has been the Northern Hemisphere; but Africa has been the point of origin of the odd subungulate types.

SOUTH AMERICAN UNGULATES

The southern continents appear to have been isolated regions for part or all of the Age of Mammals. Australia has remained disconnected and has evolved its own peculiar marsupial fauna; Africa was separated long enough to initiate the development of the subungulates but later became faunally similar to the northern continents. The history of South America is somewhat intermediate in nature. It was isolated at the dawn of the Age of Mammals and appears to have remained so until the close of the Tertiary, when connexions were renewed. During its long period of isolation many curious mammalian types developed there which are now for the most part extinct. In a previous section we mentioned the flesh-eating marsupials of that continent; in the following chapter we shall speak of the curious edentates that developed there. Here we shall touch very briefly upon the development in South America of a number of groups of ungulates which are now entirely extinct but which flourished there during Tertiary times.

When South America became separated from North America there were but few placental mammals which had then reached that continent. There were some forms ancestral to the armadillos and other edentates, perhaps some primitive monkeys, and some rodents appear to have entered later. The only other placental mammals which had penetrated were a series of primitive ungulates – small herbivorous creatures comparable to the archaic ungulate types of northern continents. No higher hoofed mammals, no true even- or odd-toed forms, were able to enter until in the Pleistocene the land connexion at Panama had become re-established. In the meantime the archaic 'old settlers' had the field to themselves and, during the Tertiary, developed into a bewildering variety of hoofed types. It is difficult to describe them without going into a maze of technical details, for all of them are now extinct, and we cannot fairly compare them with existing groups from other continents. In an accompanying figure is shown a representative selection of Miocene mammals – both of these ungulate types and their native contemporaries; the later, Pleistocene representatives of these groups were, on the average, of much larger size.

Conspicuous and numerous among the ungulates were the toxodonts, or 'bow-tooths', most of which tended to grow to large size. In general build they seem to have been somewhat like a cross between a rhinoceros and a hippopotamus. Closely related to them but very different in appearance were the little typotheres, with seemingly rodent-like habits and even, in some cases, long hopping hind legs which make a comparison with rabbits not inappropriate.

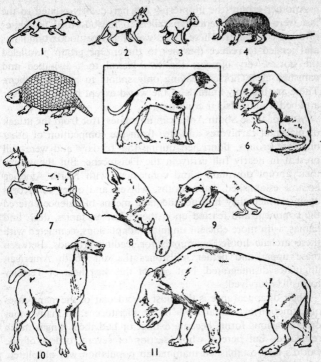

Some representative members of the mammalian fauna of South America in Miocene times to illustrate the radically different nature of the groups found there from those of other continents. A pointer dog is shown to give the scale. Representatives of most of these types survived until the Ice Age, when they had become much larger in size. The only flesh-eaters were marsupials, represented by numbers 1 and 9, which were, respectively, forms rather comparable to weasel and fox. Rodents were absent earlier in South America, but, by this time, forms related to the guinea pig had gained entrance (3). The peculiar South American edentates were already present and diversified. Besides armadillos (4), large ground sloths (6) and the armoured glyptodonts (5) were present. The remainder of the fauna consisted of ungulates of peculiar sorts. A group known as litopterns had produced such forms as a good imitation of a one-toed horse (7) and the three-toed form (10) of larger size and rather camel-like appearance. Another group of hoofed animals, known as notoungulates, had developed into a great variety of types ranging from little typotheres (2), which were rather rabbit-like in their adaptations, through the peculiar astrapotheres (8), with an elephant-like proboscis, to big toxodonts (11) which can be described only by comparing them to a blend of woodchuck and rhinoceros. (From Scott, *Land Mammals in the Western Hemisphere*, by permission of the Macmillan Co., publishers.)

Another group (the litopterns) not particularly related to the last were South American parallels to the odd-toed ungulates of other continents. These forms were fairly orthodox ungulates and tended to reduce the toes to three. One group paralleled the horses very closely; the two lateral toes dwindled and vanished as in horses, leaving only splints to represent them. These are the only animals in the world except horses that ever attained a monodactyl condition.

Most of these South American ungulates, free from the attack of placental carnivores and free from the competition of other ungulate groups, flourished during the Tertiary and were still present in nearly full array in the Pleistocene. But then came their abrupt downfall. Land connexions with North America became established. Sabretooths, wolves, and other carnivores against which they had no adequate means of defence entered the continent and feasted upon them; horses, tapirs, deer, and llamas, with more efficient ungulate adaptations, competed with these archaic hoofed mammals for feeding grounds. Between these upper and nether millstones the old South American ungulates disintegrated. Not one of this vast host of Tertiary forms has survived.

Their disappearance is the most spectacular of the many cases of extinction of animal types in the Pleistocene. In many other orders various forms became extinct or had their ranges much restricted; but here a whole section of several orders of the world's long-established mammalian population was absolutely wiped out.

CHAPTER 13

A Diversity of Mammals

AN account of the varied mammalian forms remaining for consideration before our own group, the primates, is reached would, if at all adequate, require a volume in itself. In this chapter we can give merely a brief sketch of the other major types: of the rodents, most flourishing of all mammal types; of the bats, the only flying mammals; of the whales, the most highly specialized of aquatic forms; of the curious edentates, so-called 'toothless' mammals.

RODENTS

Among the rodents, or gnawing animals, are included the squirrels, beavers, rats and mice, porcupines, guinea pigs, hares and rabbits, and hosts of less familiar forms. The rodents are without question the most successful of all living mammals. In the number of different types included in the order they exceed all other mammalian groups combined; they are found in almost every inhabitable land area of the globe and seem to thrive under almost any conditions. Their range of adaptations is a wide one. A majority of rodents are terrestrial and often burrowing types. No purely aquatic forms have developed, although the beaver and musk-rat have progressed far in this direction. Others, such as the squirrels, are arboreal; and while there are no truly flying rodents, the 'flying' squirrels have gone far along this evolutionary path. In their general bodily build the rodents are little specialized. It is their gnawing and chewing adaptations that particularly characterize the group.

The rodents are almost entirely vegetarian in their habits. There is an efficient series of grinding teeth in the cheeks. In the front of the mouth, separated from the cheek teeth by a wide gap, are the curving chisel-like gnawing teeth. Of these highly modified incisors there are typically but four – a pair in both upper and lower jaws. Subject to constant and hard use, the roots of these teeth grow continually and have their bases far back in the skull and jaw. So relentless is their growth that if, through accident or deformity, one tooth fails to meet its mate

The skull of a rodent to show the elongate, chisel-like incisors, widely separated from the cheek teeth to form the dental structure characteristic of the order as a whole.

and thus be worn off, it may keep growing outward, curve back into the mouth. prevent the jaws from closing, and eventually cause death by starvation.

Rodents may be divided, for our purposes, into four groups. Most primitive is that typified by the squirrels; the earliest well-known rodents from the Eocene were essentially squirrel-like in structure. Closely related to the true squirrels are the chipmunks, ground squirrels and gophers, and the larger woodchuck and prairie dog; the beavers, pocket gophers, and kangaroo 'rats' of the arid American regions also pertain to this group. The largest rodents ever found in the northern continents belong to the beaver family. Giant beavers were present in the Pleistocene in both Europe and North America; the American form was the size of a half-grown black bear.

Much more progressive and numerous are the rats and mice and related types which abound in almost every region of the world. They alone of all terrestrial mammals have succeeded in traversing the East Indies and entering Australia unaided by man, and, except for rabbits, are the only rodents to invade South America from the north. In addition to the numerous wild types there is the ordinary house mouse and two types of rats which have become 'domesticated' and have accompanied man into all parts of the globe.

A third great group of rodents is the one of which the porcupine and guinea pig are typical. Apart from the former animal and a few African species, the guinea-pig group is confined to South America. Until that continent became connected with North America they were the only rodents inhabiting it. A wide variety of rodents of this sort is found to-day in South America; except for the guinea pig and the chinchilla, the latter noted for its fur, most of these forms are unfamiliar to dwellers in the Northern Hemisphere. The 'water pig', or capybara, a form something like a gigantic guinea pig, grows to the size of a hog and is the largest of living rodents.

All these three groups are unquestionably fairly closely related. Widely separated from them is a fourth group including the hares and rabbits, which are characterized by the fact that in the upper jaw there is a second smaller pair of incisor teeth behind the principal ones. These forms are hence often called duplicidentates, 'duplex-toothed', in contrast to typical rodents. No connecting links between the two have ever been discovered, and it is currently thought that no real relationship exists. The rabbit type has probably achieved its gnawing specializations independently.

BATS

Only in the bats has true flight been developed by mammals. As in the pterosaurs (and in contrast with birds), the wings are formed by webs of skin; but instead of being supported by a single elongated finger, as in flying reptiles, nearly the whole

Full face and profile view of the head of a leaf-chinned bat of the West Indies. Nose and ears have grotesque sensory outgrowths which almost completely obscure the normal physiognomy. (From Anthony)

hand is involved. The thumb, a clutching organ, is free and clawed; the other fingers are all utilized in the support of the wing membrane and usually have lost their originally clawed end joints. In having the wing expanse broken by the long digits, the bat has evolved a more flexible and less easily damaged wing than that of the pterosaurs.

Bats are skilled nocturnal flyers; their ability to avoid obstacles even in pitch darkness is well known, and it is obvious that they must depend for aerial navigation upon senses other than sight. Tactile sense appears to be highly developed, and there are in many cases grotesque fleshy outgrowths about the nose and ears which appear to lodge delicate sensory structures. Hearing, however, has recently been proved to be the major reliance of the bat in avoiding obstacles. The flying bat appears to be a silent creature. But this is far from the case. The use of refined acoustic methods shows that the flying bat continuously emits a series of shrill cries which are so high pitched as to be inaudible to the human ear. The highest tones which we can hear are waves of about 20,000 vibrations per second; the bat's cries may have a frequency of about 50,000 vibrations and are thus two and a half times higher. The bat ear, however, is capable of hearing them, and the bat appears to avoid obstacles by noting the echoes reflected back from them.

The majority of bats are insect-eaters, but there is a wide range of diet, ranging from blood (in the vampire bats) to small fish. A specialized tropical group are the large fruit bats, or 'flying foxes'. Bats were developed far back in the history of mammals, for skeletons showing well-developed wing supports are found as far back as the Eocene. A possible intermediate stage in the development of flight is given in the shape of the 'flying lemur' of the East Indies. As writers on natural history have often remarked, the name is hardly appropriate, for the animal is not a lemur, nor does it fly. It does, however, have a very large fold of skin extending back from its arms by means of which it can 'plane' for a considerable distance. Probably the earliest bats began with such a type of gliding apparatus.

WHALES

The cetaceans, the whales and porpoises, constitute the largest and most important group of mammals that has turned to an aquatic life, and that best adapted to an existence in the water. They have become so completely divorced from their former land life that they are helpless if even stranded on a beach. Only in their need for air-breathing do they show any marked functional reminiscence of their previous terrestrial existence.

The cetaceans have reassumed the torpedo-like streamlined shape of primitive aquatic vertebrates; the body, however, is thick and rounded in section, and hence (unlike the typically slimmer fish) the main propulsive force is confined to the tail fin alone. As in other aquatic mammals, the tail has failed to resume its original fin structure, and, as in the sea cows, horizontal flukes supported by fibrous tissue supply the motive power. Usually in whales (as in ichthyosaurs) a fishlike dorsal fin has redeveloped. As in the sirenians, the hind legs are lost (except for internal rudiments), and the front limbs are steering flippers. Parallel, again, to the marine reptiles, extra joints may be added to the toes. Hair has been abandoned as a covering and may be absolutely lacking on the skin of the adult whale; a thick layer of fat – the blubber – affords insulation against the constant cold of the sea waters.

The teeth have been reduced in modern whales to simple peglike structures. In many forms there has been a considerable increase in numbers over the original forty-four; in others, teeth have been abandoned completely.

Some of the larger whales, such as the sperm whale, dive to great depths in pursuit of food and may remain submerged for periods of time said to be as much as forty-five minutes. It is obvious that these habits must involve major physiological specializations. The whales are adapted to withstand rapid changes between normal surface conditions and the immense pressures encountered in the depths. Without such adaptations they would suffer, as does a man under similar circumstances, from the 'bends' (pain caused by liberation of gas bubbles in the blood when pressure is decreased too suddenly). Further, there must be, and are, adaptations for taking in abnormally large supplies of oxygen before a prolonged dive.

In relation to breathing problems, the nostrils, originally of course at the front end of the snout, have moved backward over the top of the head until they open directly upward as the blowhole. The 'spouting' of the whale is the expiration of air through this peculiar type of nose when the top of the head comes to the surface of the water; the vapour seen is due to the condensation of water when the column of warm moist air blown from the lungs strikes the cooler atmosphere.

Living whales are arrayed in two major groups – the toothed whales and the whalebone whales. The former group is much the larger in numbers; teeth are generally retained, and fish and squid are the common articles of diet. The numerous varieties of porpoises and dolphins are close to the common stem of the group. Some of these toothed whales grow to great size. This is especially the case in the sperm whales, forms in which the huge blunt snout is filled by a great reservoir of sperm oil.

Sharply marked off from the toothed forms are the whalebone whales. In them teeth have been lost entirely. The huge mouth is filled with a series of sheets of whalebone fringed with hairs at the edge and hanging down from the roof of the mouth in parallel rows like the leaves of a book. This whalebone is composed of hardened skin. In the roof of the mouth of the dog, for example, may be seen crosswise ridges of skin; the whalebone has been formed by the elaboration of such a series of skin ridges.

These whalebone whales live upon plankton, small organisms in the sea water; water passing through the mouth is strained through this whalebone filter, and the edible material deposited is licked off by the tongue. It would be impossible for this type

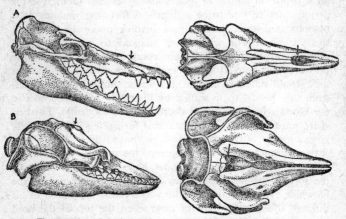

The evolution of the blowhole in whales. *A*, side and top views of the skull of a primitive cetacean, *Zeuglodon*. The external nostrils (marked by an arrow) were in a primitive position near the front end of the skull. In *B*, a typical modern cetacean, the nostrils and the bones surrounding them have shifted to the top of the skull.

of whale to swallow any large object (such as Jonah), for the gullet does not exceed nine inches in width. These whalebone whales feed upon smaller food materials than any other mammals; and it is paradoxical that they should include in their number the largest animals of any kind that have ever existed. The blue or sulphur-bottomed whale is estimated to reach a maximum weight of one hundred and fifty tons or more, being thus several times as big as the largest of known dinosaurs.

Little is known of these two whale groups before the Miocene epoch. In the Eocene, however, archaic whales, the zeuglodonts, were already common in the seas. These were, in some cases, of considerable size (seventy feet is the apparent maximum), with a body comparatively longer but slimmer than in later whales; the proportions were those which modern imagination ascribes to the sea serpent. These forms were considerably closer to their land ancestors than the typical whales. In the skull, for example, the nostrils were still near the front of the head, and the teeth were very much like those of primitive flesh-eating mammals. Not improbably the whales have come from early creodont carnivores and have gradually taken up a fish-eating existence in the same way that later otters and seals have done; but we have no fossil record of the early stages in the transition from land to water.

EDENTATES

South America is the main seat of an odd series of mammalian types usually known as the edentates – toothless mammals, including anteaters, tree sloths, and armadillos. The name is misleading for, while the anteaters are toothless, the others have a considerable number of teeth. These, however, are of a degenerate structure, being simply blocks of dentine lacking the enamel covering found in other mammals; and teeth are never present in the front of the jaws.

The South American anteaters are essentially feeders not on ordinary ants but upon termites, the 'white ants' numerous in all tropical regions. The skull is peculiarly developed for this type of diet, the snout long and slim and the jaws, in the absence of teeth, quite feeble. The mouth is merely a small terminal opening from which a long sticky tongue may be extended to gather up the insect food. The feet are armed with long, heavy, curved claws, which can dig ably into a termite nest. These claws make ordinary walking difficult, and in the front feet the claws are turned inward, the weight resting on the outer side of the knuckles.

The tree sloths of the South American forests are among the oddest of mammalian types. They are small nocturnal forms with a lichenous growth which often gives a greenish tinge to their grey hair. They are slow and clumsy, spending much of their time slothfully hanging upside down from branches and holding on by their long, curved claws, two or three in number.

These leaf-eating animals have teeth, but they comprise only four or five pairs of cylindrical pegs in either cheek.

The third living South American edentate group is that of the armadillos. As in the sloths, there are peglike cheek teeth. The interesting armadillo development, however, is the presence of armour in the shape of numerous rows of bony plates over the back and sides of the body and even over the top of the head. In the more primitive members of the group the armour forms a uniform series of movable bands the length of the body; in more advanced types the front and back parts of the shield form solid partitions over the hip and shoulder region, with movable hoops between. The armadillos are the only living mammals with a bony armour.

Besides these three living groups South America gave rise to two other and more spectacular edentate types, both extinct, the great ground sloths and the glyptodonts.

The ground sloths developed in South America in Tertiary times and reached their peak in the Pleistocene, when a number of genera were present in North America as well. One form reached the size of an elephant, and others were as large as an ox. These forms were undoubtedly related to the tree sloths but were ponderous ground dwellers. As in tree sloths and anteaters, the feet were armed with good claws; this caused a clumsy type of foot construction, which was complicated by the heavy bulk of these animals. The gait was obviously a shuffling one; the front feet rested more or less on the knuckles, the hind legs bore down on the outer edge of the broad feet. These ground sloths appear to have been able to rear up on their hind legs in bear fashion to crop leaves from the branches of trees.

Related to the armadillos were the extinct glyptodonts. They were covered with armour which here formed a solid, domed carapace covering the entire trunk. Not only was the head protected by bony plates, but the tail also was encased in a bony sheath, sometimes bearing spikes. These glyptodonts, some of them ten or more feet in length, were a close mammalian parallel to the armoured dinosaurs of the late Cretaceous.

A few small forms seemingly related to the ancestry of the South American edentates were present in North America in the Paleocene and Eocene but soon disappeared there. The ancestral edentates were marooned in South America during the Tertiary and there evolved into the five types described above. The archaic ungulates of South America were rapidly exterminated, as we have seen, with the re-establishment of North American connexions at the close of Tertiary times. The edentates, however, were of sterner stuff. They not only held their own territory during the Pleistocene but, going against the tide of migration, invaded North America; large glyptodonts are found in the Pleistocene of the Gulf coast, numerous ground sloths penetrated as far as Pennsylvania and Illinois, and even to-day the armadillos range as far north as Texas.

At the end of the Pleistocene the glyptodonts and ground sloths became extinct. The former appear to have lingered late; in the south-western United States there is positive evidence of their contemporaneity with man, and in Patagonia one appears to have been imprisoned in a cave used as a 'stall'.

In the Old World tropics are two types of termite-eaters exhibiting features similar to South American edentates. The aard-vark of Africa is a grotesque, long-eared beast which has well-developed ant-eating adaptations in the long snout, slim whiplike tongue, and powerful claws; but there the resemblance to American anteaters stops. There are peg-like teeth of peculiar construction, and the animal in general resembles nothing else at all. The term 'earth pig' is not particularly appropriate, but there is nothing with which the animal can be compared.

The pangolins of southern Asia and Africa have, again, termite-eating adaptations in the slim snout, long tongue, toothless mouth, and sharp claws. They are armoured, but not by bone; instead, there are large overlapping horny scales, giving these creatures somewhat the appearance of animated pine cones.

Neither aard-vark nor pangolin has fundamental features indicating real relationship to the true American edentates. We know little of their fossil history; presumably they represent isolated types which have taken up termite-eating as a vocation and have in relation to this tended to develop similar adaptive features.

CHAPTER 14

Primates: Lemurs, Monkeys, Apes, and Man

THE order of primates is a group of particular interest to us, for it includes not only the lemurs, monkeys, and great apes, but man himself; in the study of primate evolution we are studying our own kin, climbing our own family tree. We shall, therefore, treat the primates more fully than we have a number of other mammalian groups.

To the paleontologist the primates are a source of considerable difficulty. We have well-documented pedigrees for various mammalian types such as horses, camels, and dogs. In the case of our own ancestors we should like to present an equally adequate fossil history. Unfortunately, however, fossil remains of primates are more rare than is the case in any other large group of mammals. The reasons for this paucity of material are fairly obvious. Primates are, for the most part, tree dwellers; rock deposits in which fossil vertebrates are to be found are not normally formed in forested regions. Again, primates are mostly dwellers in the tropics, whereas most of the known Tertiary fossil beds are in what are to-day zones of temperate climate. It is only in Eocene times, when these regions (as shown by the vegetation) knew tropical conditions, that primates are found to any extent in the fossiliferous deposits of Europe and North America.

The living primates may be divided primarily into three groups: (1) the lemurs, typically small four-footed forms of rather squirrel-like appearance, found to-day in the Old World tropics and present in the Eocene in Eurasia and North America; (2) *Tarsius*, a curious small, hopping, rat-like creature from the East Indies, occupying an intermediate position between lemurs and higher primates; (3) the anthropoids,* comprising the South American monkeys, the more advanced monkeys of the Old World, the great manlike apes, and man.

* The manlike (anthropoid) apes are sometimes spoken of simply as anthropoids; but this loose usage should be avoided; the term 'Anthropoidea' properly includes monkeys as well.

ARBOREAL ADAPTATIONS

Primates are essentially arboreal, only a few forms (such as the baboons and man) having taken up a life on the ground. There

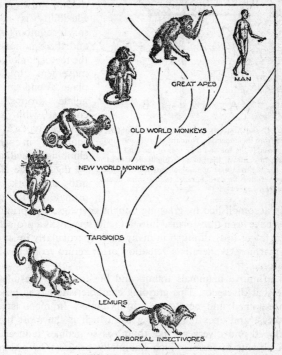

GREAT APES

MAN

OLD WORLD MONKEYS

NEW WORLD MONKEYS

TARSIOIDS

LEMURS

ARBOREAL INSECTIVORES

A simplified family tree of the primates.

is considerable evidence suggesting that the primitive placentals were tree dwellers to begin with and that the primates have merely continued on in this ancestral track. Arboreal life is apparently responsible for much of the progressive development of primate characteristics; and, although man is not a tree dweller, this life of his ancestors has left its mark deeply upon him and is perhaps in great measure responsible for the attainment of his present estate.

LIMBS. Locomotion in the tree has left the skeleton of the

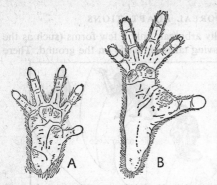

primates in a condition much closer to that of the primitive placentals than is the case in most groups. Flexibility is necessary for climbing trees, and there is none of the restriction of limb movement to one plane found in ungulate groups. In contrast with such arboreal types as the squirrels, in which climbing is facilitated by digging the claws into the bark, the primate hold is generally accomplished by grasping boughs or twigs. The primitive claws have been transformed into flat nails serving as a protection to the finger tips, although in many cases (particularly in lemurs and marmosets) there is a retention of or return to a claw-like structure.

Hand (*A*) and foot (*B*) of an Old World monkey; viewed from the underside. Note the short thumb and the opposable big toe and long toes of the hind foot. In man, in contrast, the thumb is highly developed, while the big toe (once opposable) has, with upright posture, shifted forward parallel to the other toes. (From Pocock)

In primitive mammals thumb and big toe were presumably somewhat divergent. This grasping characteristic has in general been retained and emphasized in primates. In most lemurs, monkeys, and apes it is the big toe which is the most highly developed and divergent; the thumb is sometimes reduced, or even absent, in forms which habitually progress by swinging from branch to branch, the other four fingers here hooking over the bough and the thumb being not only useless but actually in the way. Otherwise there has been almost no reduction of toes; the primates are in this respect more conservative than most mammalian groups.

Four-footed locomotion is the rule among primates, bipedal tendencies becoming apparent for the most part only among the higher members of the order. The hands, however, while primarily possessing their grasping adaptation in relation to locomotion, are well adapted (in contrast to most mammals) for grasping food and other objects; and even among the lemurs there is a tendency towards a sitting posture and the release of the front feet from supporting the body.

The primitively long tail is retained in almost all the lower primates and is apparently of considerable use in balancing. In many South American monkeys it has developed into a prehensile 'fifth hand'. In a number of cases, however, the tail is reduced or absent, and there is no external tail in the manlike apes and man.

TEETH. An omnivorous diet appears to have been general in early primates, and similar food habits characterize many living types (although there has been a strong herbivorous trend). The dentition is, hence, usually less specialized than in most mammalian groups; the molar teeth are low-crowned with rounded cusps. In diet primates are not dissimilar to the swine, and the cheek teeth of these two groups are fairly similar; indeed the teeth of a fossil native pig from Nebraska were for a time mistakenly identified as those of a manlike American ape. In all primates, including man, the number of incisor teeth has been reduced from the original three to two in each half of each jaw, and there has also been a trend towards reduction in the number of premolar ('bicuspid') teeth from four to two, so that the higher monkeys and man have but thirty-two teeth instead of the forty-four present in our primitive placental ancestors. Primates are in general short-jawed and, consequently, short-faced types. In most of them the canine teeth are rather long and make effective biting weapons; in man, however, they have ceased to project above the general level of the tooth row.

SENSE ORGANS. Arboreal life has had a profound effect upon the sense organs. A ground-dwelling mammal is in great measure dependent upon smell for his knowledge of things about him, and his nostrils are highly developed, while sight is usually comparatively poor. The reverse is true in these arboreal types. For locomotion in the tree good eyesight is essential, and throughout the primate group there has been a progressive series of advances in the visual apparatus. Even in the lemurs the eyes are large, and there is a tendency to rotate them forward from their primitive lateral position. This results in a situation where parts of the two fields of vision overlap, and in *Tarsius* and the higher primates the two fields are identical. In vertebrates below the mammals the eyes appear to furnish the brain with two separate visual images. In mammals where the fields overlap, there typically arises the stereoscopic type of vision, well developed in the higher primates. In this condition there is a sorting-out of the nerve fibres running from eye to brain, so that the brain pictures formed by the two eyes coincide, and the minute variation between the two pictures gives the effect of depth. In addition, the monkeys and all higher types possess in the middle of each retina a specialized region, the 'central pit' (*fovea centralis*), in which detail is much more clearly perceived.

With this improvement in vision goes a corresponding degeneration of the sense of smell. Even in the lemurs the olfactory sense is reduced, and in the manlike apes and man it is probably in the most rudimentary state to be found in any terrestrial placental.

BRAIN. The brain, as well, has been profoundly influenced by arboreal life. Locomotion in the trees requires great agility and muscular co-ordination; this co-ordination in itself demands development of the brain centres; and it is of interest that much of the higher mental faculties is apparently developed in an area alongside the motor centres of the brain. Again, the development of good eyesight rendered possible for primates a far wider acquisition of knowledge of their environment than is possible for forms which depend upon smell. Perhaps still more important in the evolution of primate mentality has been the development of the grasping hand as a sensory aid in the examination of objects.

A constantly increasing brain size has been a characteristic feature of primate development. The cerebral hemispheres have grown in size and in all the higher Anthropoidea completely cover the cerebellum. Among the smaller monkeys are to be found the highest relative weights of brain to body in any mammals.

SKULL. These changes in dentition, sense organs, and brain have been associated with great changes in the primate head. Most lemurs have an elongate skull of primitive appearance, with a long face and a long, low braincase. But with the reduction of the sense of smell and the concurrent abbreviation of the tooth row, the muzzle in most primates has shortened considerably, the face sloping sharply downward towards the mouth.

While the face has been reduced, the braincase has, on the contrary, expanded greatly in higher primates to accommodate the ever growing brain. In primitive mammals there was no bone separating the eye socket from the temple region. In a number of mammalian types a superficial bar has been built between these two openings. Such a bar is present in all primates from the very first. But, in addition, monkeys, apes, and men have built up underneath this a solid partition between eye and temple. This is unique among animals. Presumably it gives a better attachment and support for the eyes in their rotated position and also prevents the jaw muscles, pushed out sideways by the expanding brain, from crowding forward into the eye sockets.

LEMURS

Most primitive of primates are the lemurs, found to-day in tropical Asia and Africa, more especially on the island of Madagascar. An ordinary Madagascar lemur of to-day is a fairly small arboreal animal, nocturnal in habits, with a bushy, hairy covering which contrasts with the rather sparse coat of most higher primates. The limbs are moderately long, the ears pointed, and the eyes are directed more laterally than forward. The lemur face may undergo some shortening, but it is in most cases a comparatively long and foxlike muzzle. The tail, usually long, is never a grasping organ. Thumb and big toe are always widely separable from the other digits; the big toe is especially well developed and has a flat nail in all forms, whereas the other digits are variable in their covering. Typical lemurs have a clawlike nail on the second toe but normal nails on the other digits.

The reason for the survival of these primitive forms on the island of Madagascar is seemingly the fact that this area has been long separated from the mainland of Africa, and, in consequence, but few flesh-eaters have been able to enter this region; members of the civet family are the lemurs' only enemies.

On the mainlands, on the contrary, lemurs are extremely scarce. In southern Asia there are two species of loris, and in tropical Africa are the potto and 'bush baby' (*Galago*), all somewhat more advanced types than the typical Madagascar forms.

In the Eocene, lemurs not unlike the living Madagascar types were common in both Europe and North America. Beyond the Eocene, however, they vanish from the fossil record of the northern regions, which presumably were already becoming a bit too chilly for tropical forms.

The lemurs are exceedingly primitive primates and not far removed from the tree-shrew types from which the primates appear to have arisen. Indeed, so primitive are they, that some writers have believed that they should not be considered as primates at all but as progressive insectivores.

TARSIUS

Much higher in the scale of primate evolution than any lemur is *Tarsius*, a small nocturnal tree dweller from the East Indies. He has a peculiar ratlike tail and long hind legs adapted for a hopping gait. These are specialized features in which *Tarsius* is off the main evolutionary line of primates. But the rest of the beast's structures are curiously intermediate between lemur and monkey types.

The brain is large, and the braincase is short and rounded. The visual apparatus is much advanced over that of the lemurs. The eyes are exceptionally large and are turned completely forward from the primitive lateral position, with the orbits close together above the nose. In this creature the two fields of vision are identical, and recent work indicates that stereoscopic vision is well developed.

While vision has thus advanced, the sense of smell has been proportionately reduced. The foxlike snout of the typical lemur has disappeared, and the nose has shrunken to a small nubbin tucked in between and below the eyes. There is little projection of the muzzle (the tooth row is comparatively short), and we have here the beginning of the type of face found in monkeys, apes, and man.

An interesting feature in which *Tarsius* shows affinities with the higher primates is the fact that the placental connexions between mother and young, instead of being distributed, as in lemurs, all about the surface of the sac containing the embryo, are concentrated in one discoidal area and shed at birth just as in monkeys and men.

Tarsius is not a monkey, but it is far above the lemur level. The living form is too specialized in itself to be a true intermediate

type, but it seems not unreasonable to regard it as an offshoot
of a group transitional from lemurs to monkeys. In confirmation
of the suggestion is the fact that in the Eocene, as contemporaries
of the early lemurs, are found remains of numerous *Tarsius*-like
animals which appear to bridge the gap between lemurs and
higher primates.

MONKEYS

With the monkeys we reach the third and highest main division
of the primate group, that of the anthropoids, or manlike
creatures in a broad sense, including monkeys, the great apes,
and man.

MONKEY CHARACTERS. In all these forms we have a very
distinct general advance upon the types already discussed. The
eyes are large and placed far forward as was already the case in
Tarsius. But, in addition, a special area (*fovea centralis*) in the
centre of the eye making for clear perception of detail is developed
in even the lowest of monkeys; the monkey's eye is already on a
par with our own. With this increase in vision we find, as we
would expect, that smell is unimportant and the snout usually
much reduced.

The monkey is normally a four-footed walker, but there is a
great tendency for an upright sitting posture and the consequent
freeing of the hands for the manipulation of food and other
objects. The brain is comparatively large in all members of the
group, and the much-swollen braincase gives the skull a rather
human shape. The freeing of the hands and the perfection of the
visual apparatus undoubtedly give much greater scope to the
higher mental status found in even the lowest monkeys. We
speak proverbially of 'monkey curiosity'. This monkey trait is
probably due in great measure to the fact that the monkey has
good eyesight; he can see more to be curious about. Then, too,
he has a great advantage in a means of satisfying his curiosity
not possible in most animals; he can handle the objects seen.

We speak often, with respect, of scientific research. But, after
all, what is research but the same old urge of the monkey to
handle some new or curious thing? It may well be on a higher
plane, but it is the same monkey curiosity which has made our
simian relatives the pests of the jungle.

The anthropoids are readily divisible into two groups. On the one hand, are the South American monkeys (platyrrhines); on the other, are Old World monkeys, the great apes, and man (catarrhines).

NEW WORLD MONKEYS. The South American forms are generally known as platyrrhines, or 'flat-nosed' monkeys, owing to the fact that the nostrils are widely separated and look more sideways than forward or downward. If we wish a further technical character we may note that in these New World monkeys there are three premolar teeth in each half of each jaw, whereas in all the Old World forms, as in man, but two such teeth are present.

The smaller forms among the South American monkeys are the marmosets. These little fellows are squirrel-like in general appearance, with thick fur and a bushy tail, and are, except for the short face, rather like the lemurs superficially. Some writers have suggested that the marmosets are really primitive monkeys close to the lemur ancestors. Others, however, believe that their seeming primitiveness is due to specialization and degeneration. As an example of marmoset specialization may be mentioned the fact that the last molar has disappeared. In man this molar, the 'wisdom tooth', is degenerate and often fails to function; but with its total loss the marmosets have progressed farther than we have in this one regard.

Much more typical monkeys are also present in South and Central America; of these the organ-grinder's monkey, the capuchin, is a typical representative. In a majority of these forms the tail is not only long but has developed into a prehensile organ, a 'fifth hand' of great utility. Some members of this group, the spider monkeys, are very clever acrobats, while an interesting side branch is that of the howler monkeys. These have a large, bony, resonating chamber in the throat; by means of the sounds emanating from it, night is made mournful in the South American forests.

Little is known of the fossil history of these American monkeys. They are certainly on a lower plane of organization than the Old World forms. But there is little to indicate that this group lies on the main line of descent of the higher primates, and their evolution may have occurred parallel to that of the monkeys of the Eastern Hemisphere.

CATARRHINE CHARACTERS. Grouped as the catarrhines

are the monkeys of Asia and Africa, the manlike apes, and man. The name indicates one of the many features in which they are more advanced than the South American monkeys – the fact that the nostrils are closer together and open forward and down. There is a rather general tendency towards an increase in size, which culminates in the chimpanzee, man, and gorilla. Although primitively arboreal, some of the higher or more specialized types, as man and the baboons, tend towards a terrestrial life. The tail is often shortened or absent. Primitively four-footed, some have tended to an arm-swinging type of locomotion in which the body is held erect; man has attained an erect posture. Although progression on the ground is usually on all fours, the long arms bring the back into a slanting position, while sitting is the common catarrhine pose when not in motion. The thumb is usually well developed and opposable, and the big toe universally so except where secondarily modified in man. The hairy covering is always thin and the face naked.

The brain is large. The face, primitively short, tends to elongate in some instances in correlation with a tendency towards a vegetable diet and a consequent increase in tooth size. There are only two premolar teeth in each jaw half; we have finally arrived at the stage of reduction still found in man, with only thirty-two teeth instead of the original forty-four.

OLD WORLD MONKEYS. Anthropoids date back to the beginning of the Oligocene epoch in the Old World. In fossil beds of that age in the Fayum district of Egypt have been found a jaw and a few other fragments which, while incomplete, are enough to show us that small, primitive, Old World monkeys had evolved by that time. From these early forms may have descended the numerous Old World monkeys of the present.

These monkeys include a great variety of forms, with a wide range in structures and habits. All are, in terrestrial locomotion, four-footed types walking flat on palm and sole. Correlated with the common sitting posture is the universal presence in these monkeys of hardened skin areas, sitting pads (callosities), on the buttocks. The more primitive monkeys are arboreal, but the baboons and their relatives show a progressive tendency towards a ground-dwelling life.

Two groups of living Old World monkeys are easily distinguishable to-day: one group having cheek pouches for the

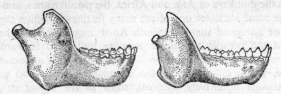

Left, the jaw of *Parapithecus* of the Oligocene of Egypt, oldest known monkey. Length of original about 1½ inches. *Right*, the jaw of *Propliopithecus*, oldest known manlike ape, from the same beds. Length of original about 2¾ inches. (After Schlosser)

storage of food, the other having a complicated type of stomach, somewhat comparable to that of ruminants, for the digestion of vegetable fodder.

To the cheek-pouched group belong most of the small African tree dwellers seen frequently in our zoos – green monkey, mona monkey, etc. Somewhat more specialized are the macaques – the rhesus monkey and its allies – mainly Asiatic forms but including the barbary ape, present on the rock of Gibraltar and the only monkey inhabiting Europe. The macaques are less arboreal in habits than the common African monkeys, and the face is somewhat longer, for the grinding teeth have tended to lengthen with development of better chewing power. From the macaques several intermediate types lead to the baboons and their hideous cousins, the drills and mandrills. These largest of monkeys have become as purely ground dwellers as has man; but they have become four-footed ground types, walking flat on palm and sole. In relation to their herbivorous mode of life, the tooth row has become elongated, and, consequently, the doglike face here resembles, secondarily, the old snout of the primitive mammals.

The second Old World monkey group, that of forms with a complicated stomach and no cheek pouches, has as central types the langurs of southern Asia, such as the sacred hanuman monkey of India. All these forms are good arboreal types, showing none

Head of an adult male proboscis monkey (*Nasalis larvatus*). (From Pocock)

of the ground-dwelling tendencies of the cheek-pouched monkeys. An interesting variant in this group is the proboscis monkey with, in old males particularly, a long pendant nose which outdoes that of man in its development.

MANLIKE APES

But the Old World monkey groups, interesting as they are in showing how monkeys can vary in structure and adaptations, have little to do with our own history. Our ancestors came from a third line of monkey evolution, one leading to the development of the anthropoid apes. This line diverged from that of the modern monkeys at a very early date, for in the same Egyptian beds where are found the earliest known monkeys occurs the jaw of a small ancestral anthropoid ape.

STRUCTURE OF THE GREAT APES. The anthropoid, or manlike ape group, includes four living types: the gibbon, the orangoutan, the chimpanzee, and the gorilla. All are of good size, ranging from the comparatively small gibbons to gorillas several times as heavy as a man. The skeleton is rather close to the human type. The chest is broad, in contrast to the thin, deep chest of monkeys and of mammals in general. The hands are fairly similar to those of man, but the fingers are generally quite long in comparison with the thumb, and the arms are much elongated; the legs, on the contrary, are short. The foot is still an excellent grasping structure, with the toes long and the big toe opposable to the others in handlike fashion.

These features, particularly those of the arms, seem to be associated with the great-ape type of locomotion. With increasing weight, four-footed running along a single branch becomes increasingly difficult. The weight may be distributed if the ape rests his feet on one branch and grasps an overlying one with his arms. From this it is but a step to the type of locomotion in which these forms, particularly the gibbons and orang, are adept. These apes swing by the hands from bough to bough much as one swings along the travelling rings in a gymnasium. The feet are so definitely adapted to a grasping function that most great apes cannot walk flat on their soles but must support their weight on the outer side of the foot.

It will be noted that in swinging by the arms the body is necessarily held erect. There is but little tendency for the use of the erect posture when on the ground. But the front legs of all these apes being much longer than the hind, the body is necessarily tilted up considerably in front even in four-footed walking. Erect posture, an essentially human character, thus has its beginnings among these tree-dwelling types.

The brain is large, especially in the gorillas, but its growth has not kept up proportionately with increase in bodily bulk, and its relatively small size is in great measure responsible for the rather ferocious appearance of such a form as the gorilla, with its low forehead and beetling brow ridges. There is, as in most mammals, no projecting chin, the jaw sloping away under the lips. The grinding teeth tend to be rather heavy and elongate, giving more of a projecting face than in man, and the canine teeth are prominent.

GIBBONS. Smallest and most primitive of anthropoid apes are the gibbons (including hoolock and siamang) of the Malay region. The ordinary gibbon does not exceed three feet or so in standing posture. Alone among living anthropoids these small apes customarily walk erect when on the ground, with the extremely long arms used as balancers. But this type of loco-motion is comparatively rare, for the gibbon is a highly developed arboreal acrobat capable of feats which no circus artist could attempt to imitate. The brain cavity has a capacity of about 90 c.c. In a modern European the comparable figure is about 1,500 c.c. The gibbon is, unquestionably, a much less intelligent creature than man (or the other higher apes), but we must take into account also the fact that we are dealing with a much smaller creature. We find that in two or more animals of equal intelligence the brains vary somewhat (although not directly proportionately) with body size.

Fragmentary remains of gibbon-like forms are found in the mid-Tertiary of the Old World, and it would seem probable that, except for features (such as long arms) related to the gibbon's excessively great adaptations to a gymnastic life, this form is a comparatively little modified descendant of the most primitive, extinct, manlike apes.

ORANGOUTAN. Next above the gibbons in the scale of living primates is the orangoutan, the 'wild man' of Borneo and Sumatra. This red-haired beast is considerably larger than the gibbon, adult males reaching nearly five feet in height. The orang brain is very much larger than that of the gibbon, reaching a maximum of over 500 c.c. in capacity. There is no development of heavy brow ridges and the consequent ferocity of appearance which we get in the gorillas and to a lesser extent in the chimpanzees; the eyes are set close together above the deeply concave nasal region, giving a type of face quite unlike that of other apes. The orang is, again, a good arboreal type, with long arms which can reach the ankles in the erect position.

This ape, while obviously above the gibbon in station, is probably far off the line leading to the two higher manlike apes and man, and but little is known of its fossil history.

HIGHER MANLIKE APES – CHIMPANZEE AND GORILLA. Thus far our primate history has with few exceptions been one of increasing adaptation to arboreal life. But our present knowledge, small as it is, leads us to believe that by Miocene times a new tendency was already beginning, the first traces of a return from the trees to the ground. Three living creatures are descendants of the ancestral forms in which this trend first appeared. Two forms, the chimpanzee and the gorilla, have not gone far with this process of terrestrial adaptation, nor have they met with great success; a third form, man, has succeeded.

The great African apes, the chimpanzees and gorillas, are quite similar to each other in many respects and are obviously closely related. Both these living types are less pronounced in their arboreal adaptations than the lower apes and monkeys. The chimpanzee is more at home on the ground than are the gibbons and orangs but is still essentially a tree dweller. The gorilla, on the other hand, is (particularly as regards the highland type from central Africa) essentially a ground dweller and takes to the trees but little. In both forms the arms are much shorter than in the lower manlike apes but are still quite long as compared with any human standards. Both are large animals, the chimpanzee reaching as much as five feet in height, the male gorilla six feet, and, it is said, sometimes a weight of six hundred pounds in an old male.

Brains are comparatively well developed in these great apes. That in an exceptional gorilla may attain a maximum of 630 c.c.; this is halfway to the average of certain human races. And intelligence, too, is increasing. Recently there has been considerable experimental work done by psychologists in testing the mentality of these forms, particularly the chimpanzee. They seem to show the rudiments of a human type of intelligence. There is a good memory, but, more than that, there seem to be the beginnings of reasoning powers of human type. For example, instead of merely jumping blindly and vainly for food suspended out of reach as an ordinary animal might do, the chimpanzee may, of its own volition, attempt to pile up boxes to stand on or fit together sticks with which to knock the food down.

The chimpanzee and gorilla thus have tended towards ground dwelling (although not as bipeds) and towards a human type of mentality. These are features which would be expected in human ancestors. Neither of these living apes, obviously, is a direct ancestor of man, but the evidence suggests strongly that we are here dealing with members of a group of animals from which man might well have descended.

FOSSIL APES. What does the fossil record give us by way of an answer to this surmise? The answer must, at the present time, unfortunately be but a limited and qualified one. In the Miocene and Pliocene rocks of the Old World, chiefly in the Siwalik Hills of India, we find fragmentary remains of large primates. To most of them is applied the scientific name of *Dryopithecus*, the 'oak ape', so-called because of the presence of oak leaves in the deposits from which the first remains of this form were obtained. The finds consist almost entirely of teeth and jaws. This is disappointing; but, fortunately, teeth are the most characteristic parts of any animal, and these teeth and jaws have been carefully studied. Of these fragments we can say that they possess features found to-day in but three mammals – the chimpanzee, the gorilla, and man. Some of them show characters which tend to make us believe that they are ancestral to the gorilla or chimpanzee. Some apparently represent short sterile twigs of the anthropoid-ape family tree. And some show tendencies which might well have led in a human direction. Beyond this we cannot go. We cannot say definitely that any known fossil of this age represents the actual manlike primate from which man took his origin.

The fossil record of Tertiary tropical life is, however, still comparatively unknown. It is not only possible but extremely probable that the Asiatic hills will, upon further exploration, give us the certain knowledge we desire of the primate ancestors of man.

SOUTH AFRICAN MANLIKE APES. Highly suggestive are a number of ape fossils discovered in recent years in South Africa (by Dart and Broom). These have been found in limestone quarries of Pleistocene age and hence are a bit too late to be considered as actual human ancestors. They nevertheless show features approaching man much more closely than any other apes, living or dead.

First discovered was a skull to which the name *Australopithecus* – 'southern ape' – was given. Part of the braincase had been lost, but this was rather an advantage than otherwise, for its removal exposed a cast of much of the brain. The individual was a baby ape, for the stage of eruption of the teeth is that corresponding to a human child of six or seven. The youth of the specimen was an unfortunate feature, for the differences between a young ape and the human infant are much less obvious than differences between the adults. The creature was certainly below human standards, for estimates of brain size indicate that it was of ape rather than human volume. However, the youngster differs markedly from chimpanzees and gorillas of similar age. The teeth, particularly, showed many human features. It was hence claimed that *Australopithecus* was a very advanced ape type approaching, although not reaching, the human level.

This claim appears to be substantiated by later discoveries of adult skulls from other quarries in the Transvaal. These differ slightly from the first find and hence have been given different names – *Plesianthropus*, *Paranthropus* – but seem to be closely related, at any rate. Although the new materials had also been damaged before their discovery, there is enough to enable us to restore most of the skull with confidence, and there is much of the jaw and a few other fragments. As was deduced from the *Australopithecus* specimen, the contours of the adult skulls are, on the whole, rather more like those of ape than man, and the face in side view has the concave ape profile, without the projecting human nose bones. On the other hand, the brain capacity has been estimated in two specimens at 450 and 650 c.c., respectively. The latter figure exceeds the largest capacity recorded in any known ape. Strong indications of human relationships are found in the dentition. In apes the teeth are arranged essentially as if forming three sides of an oblong, the two grinder series parallel to each other and the projecting canines forming the angles at the front. In man the canines do not project, and the whole tooth row forms a horseshoe-shaped curve. In *Plesianthropus* the tooth row is curved, and the canines are nearly as small as in man. Further, the details of the other teeth and their cusp patterns are quite close to the human pattern.

As we have said, these 'southern apes' are probably contemporaries of the oldest known men and hence cannot be actual ancestors. They seem, however, to represent a structural stage just preceding that of man and may well be the conservative descendants of the immediate human ancestor.

FROM APE TO MAN

The gulf between the great apes and a modern man seems to us a huge one, but, as a matter of fact, the anatomical features which distinguish men from apes are comparatively few. Bone for bone, muscle for muscle, organ for organ, almost every feature of the ape is repeated in the human body. The differences are almost entirely differences in proportions and relations of parts; the structures are almost identical.

The differences are related mainly to locomotor habits and brain growth. Among the higher apes we have seen trends towards erect posture and towards terrestrial life; man alone has carried out these tendencies to their logical conclusion and has become a ground-dwelling biped. His arms, not used for swinging from the branches, are comparatively short. It is highly improbable that we have descended from forms with as long arms as the gibbon or orang; our arms have, and probably have always had, the more normal proportions of those of the lower primates, while the great apes which have become permanent tree dwellers have tended to long arms but short legs. The human hand, except for its somewhat greater flexibility, is of a primitive primate type, while the living great apes have tended to elongate the fingers, except the thumb, for hooking over branches.

A greater difference between man and other primates lies in the foot. In the great apes, as in primates generally, the foot, like the hand, is an efficient grasping structure. But this is an awkward affair for ground life, particularly in a biped where the feet must bear the entire weight of the body. In man the toes have shortened, the big toe has been brought into line with the others, and the heel bone is expanded for a prop at the back (this last feature was already partially developed in the great apes). In the evolution of erect posture the backbone has become more sinuously curved than in the apes, with the result of bringing the trunk and head directly above the hips and centring the weight over the legs.

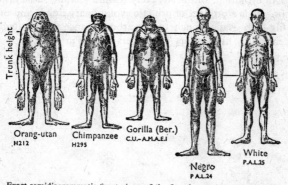

Exact semidiagrammatic front views of the four largest primates at fully adult age, constructed from detailed measurements on actual specimens, drawn without the hair, all reduced to the same trunk height. The proportionate differences between man and the great apes lie mainly in the construction of head and neck, breadth of trunk, and leg length. Note particularly that, while we think of the apes as long-armed, this is not the case with chimpanzee or gorilla; the legs have shortened, but the arms are not proportionately long. (From A. H. Schultz)

In the great apes there is more of a muzzle than in man, for the teeth are more powerful and longer; the canines, too, project. In man the teeth are less powerfully developed and the face shortened, the nose becoming prominent with this reduction and the chin developing. This dental degeneration may perhaps be correlated with the freeing of the hands as aids in feeding.

Outstanding, of course, has been the development of the brain. In modern human races the average brain size ranges, roughly, from about 1,200 to 1,500 c.c., or, on the average, two to three times that of the great apes. This difference has, of course, been responsible for many changes in the proportions of the skull and the general appearance of the head, the reduction of the heavy eyebrow ridges, and the development in their place of a high forehead. Brains have been responsible for giving man, otherwise a rather feeble creature, the place in the world which he now occupies. But, except in size and the great development of certain areas which are presumed to be the seat of the higher mental faculties, every feature of the human brain finds its parallel in the brain of the great apes.

Man has gone far and, we trust, may go still farther along new lines of evolution. But in his every feature – brain, sense organs, limbs – he is a product of primate evolutionary trends and owes, in his high estate, much to his arboreal ancestry, to features developed by his Tertiary forefathers for life in the trees.